Zaner-Bloser
Handwriting

g go

ZB Zaner-Bloser
The Language Arts and Reading Company

Credits

Art: Bernard Adnet/Craven Design: 4, 18–19, 22–23, 26–27, 30–31, 34–35, 37–38, 110–112, 129–137, 141 (top); Jack Pullan/StoryBook Arts, Inc.: 6, 40, 114, 128; Nathan Jarvis: 8, 10, 48, 56, 57–63, 64, 65–71, 82, 92, 100, 108, 109; Kyle Poling/Liz Sanders Agency: 41–47, 49–55; Tim Beaumont/Painted Words: 73–81, 83–91, 93–99, 101–107, 140, 141 (bottom); Nomar Perez/Painted Words: 115–126; Mircea Catusanu/Painted Words: 138

Literature: "I Like to Go to School" by Lois Lenski, from All Around Me by Lois Lenski. ©1968 by Lois Lenski. published by Sterling Lord Literistic. All rights reserved.; "Dogs" From Around and About by Marchette Chute, published 1957 by E. P. Dutton. Copyright renewed by Marchette Chute, 1985. Reprinted by permission of Elizabeth Hauser.

Photos: ©Frans Lanting/Corbis: Cover; ©iStockphoto.com/Belknap: 5; George C. Anderson Photography, Inc.: 14–15; ©Frank Gaglione/Getty Images: 39; ©Benjamin Shearn/Getty Images: 113; ©Annabelle Breakey/Photolibrary: 127

ISBN 978-0-7367-6835-1   13 14 15 16 17   997   14 13 12 11 10

SUSTAINABLE FORESTRY INITIATIVE — Certified Chain of Custody — Promoting Sustainable Forestry — www.sfiprogram.org — SFI-00712

CONTENTS

Zaner-Bloser

Unit 4 Using What You Have Learned

Unit 3 Writing Numerals

I Like to Go to School

I like to go to school,
    I want to read a book,
I want to learn the words
    And at the pictures look.

I want to learn to write,
    I like to make my name;
And when it comes recess,
    Run out to play a game.

I want to learn to count,
    Add numbers in a row;
I study hard at school,
    That's where I like to go!

Lois Lenski

Help Marco find his school.

FISH	ELEPHANT	DUCK	CAMEL	BEAR	ANT
LION	KITE	JAM	INSECTS	HEN	GUITAR
RAINBOW	QUILT	PIG	OCTOPUS	NEST	MOON
FOX	WAGON	VASE	UMBRELLA	TRAIN	SUN
				ZEBRA	YO-YO

a	b	c	d	e	f
g	h	i	j	k	l
m	n	o	p	q	r
s	t	u	v	w	x
y	z				

fish	elephant	duck	camel	bear	ant
lion	kite	jam	insects	hen	guitar
rainbow	quilt	pig	octopus	nest	moon
fox	wagon	vase	umbrella	train	sun
				zebra	yo-yo

Show What You Can Do

Draw a picture.

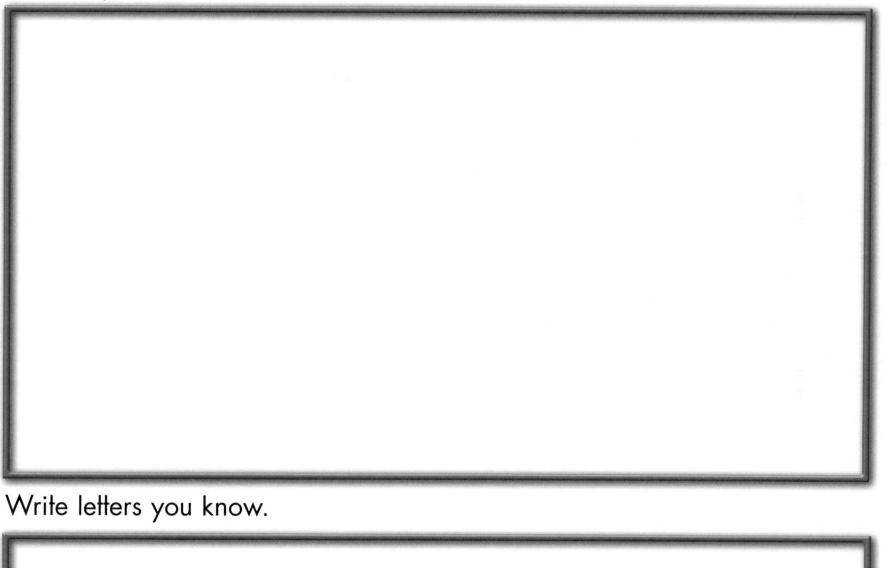

Write letters you know.

You use your hands when you write.

Trace your **left** hand on this mitten.

Many children use their left hand to write.

Trace your **right** hand on this mitten.

Which hand do you use to hold your pencil?

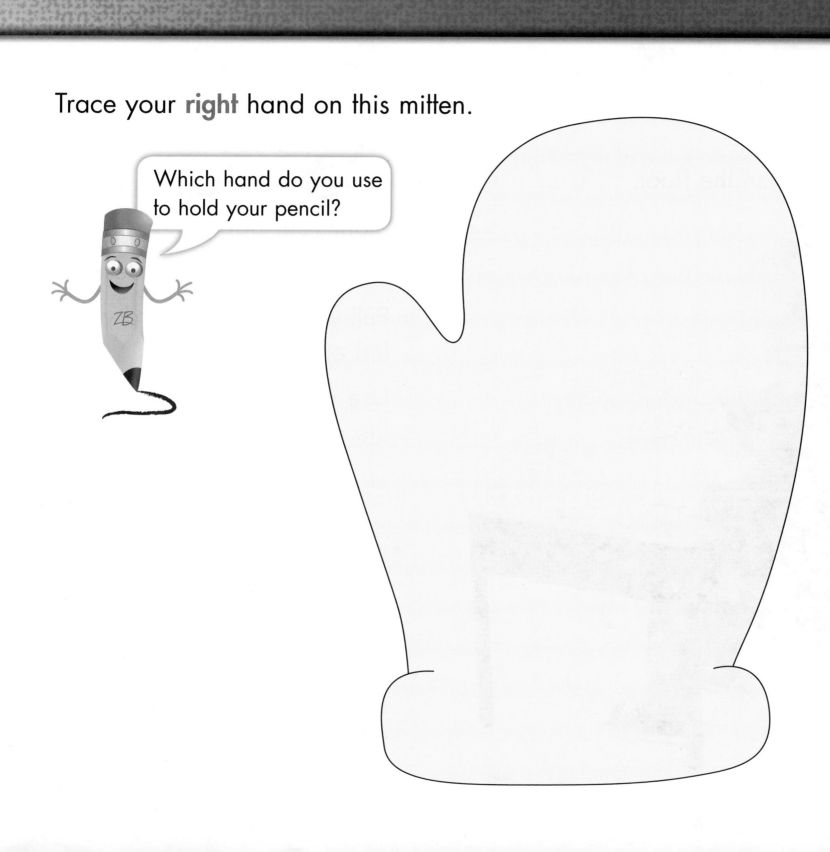

If you write with your  left hand . . .

Sit up tall.
Keep your feet on the floor.

Slant your paper.

Put both arms on the desk.

Pull your pencil toward your left elbow.

Use your right hand to move the paper.

Hold the pencil like this.

Do not squeeze the pencil when you write.

If you write with your  right hand . . .

Sit up tall.
Keep both feet on the floor.

Keep your paper straight.

Put both arms on the desk.

Pull your pencil toward the middle of your body.

Use your left hand to move the paper.

Hold the pencil like this.

Do not squeeze the pencil when you write.

Your Book

Look for these in your handwriting book.

Arrows show how to write letters.

The colored lines will help you write.

← Headline

← Midline

← Baseline

Start at the green dot. ●

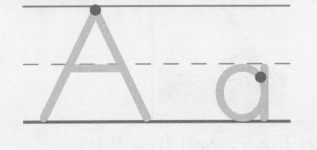

Stop and circle the best letter you wrote.

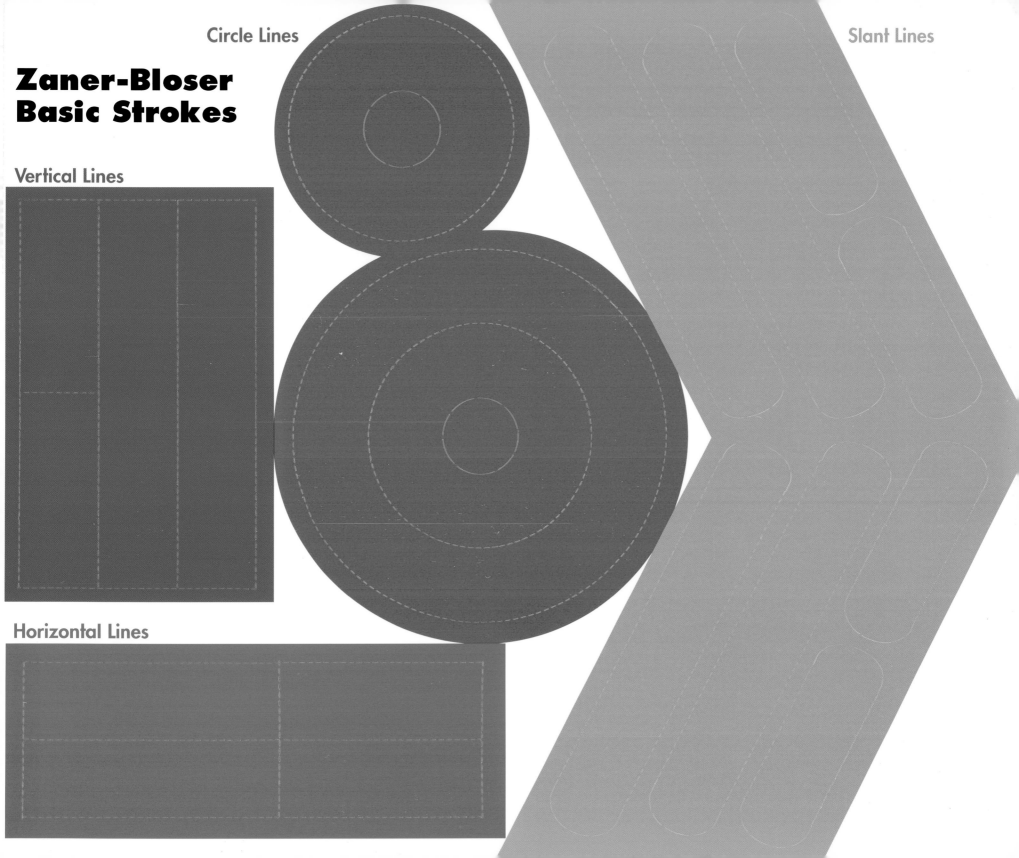

Zaner-Bloser
Basic Strokes

Circle Lines

Slant Lines

Vertical Lines

Horizontal Lines

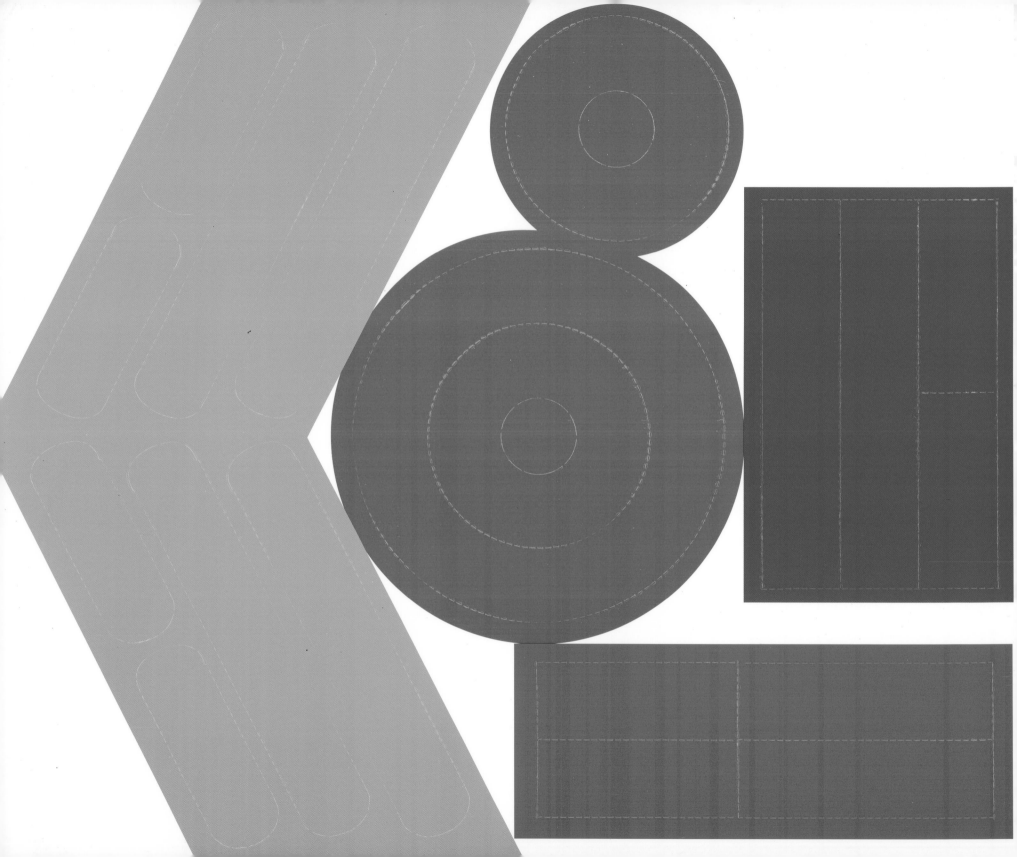

Vertical Lines

You use vertical lines when you write.
Place your vertical strokes below.
Trace them with your finger.

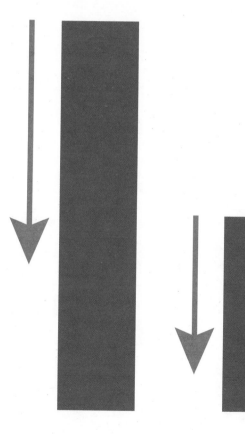

Find vertical lines in the picture above.
Draw this picture or one of your own.

Write vertical lines.
Start at the ●. Stop at the ●.

Vertical Lines

Write vertical lines.

Start at the ●. Stop at the ●.

Trace the lines.

Use your finger to trace the vertical lines
in the letters and numerals.

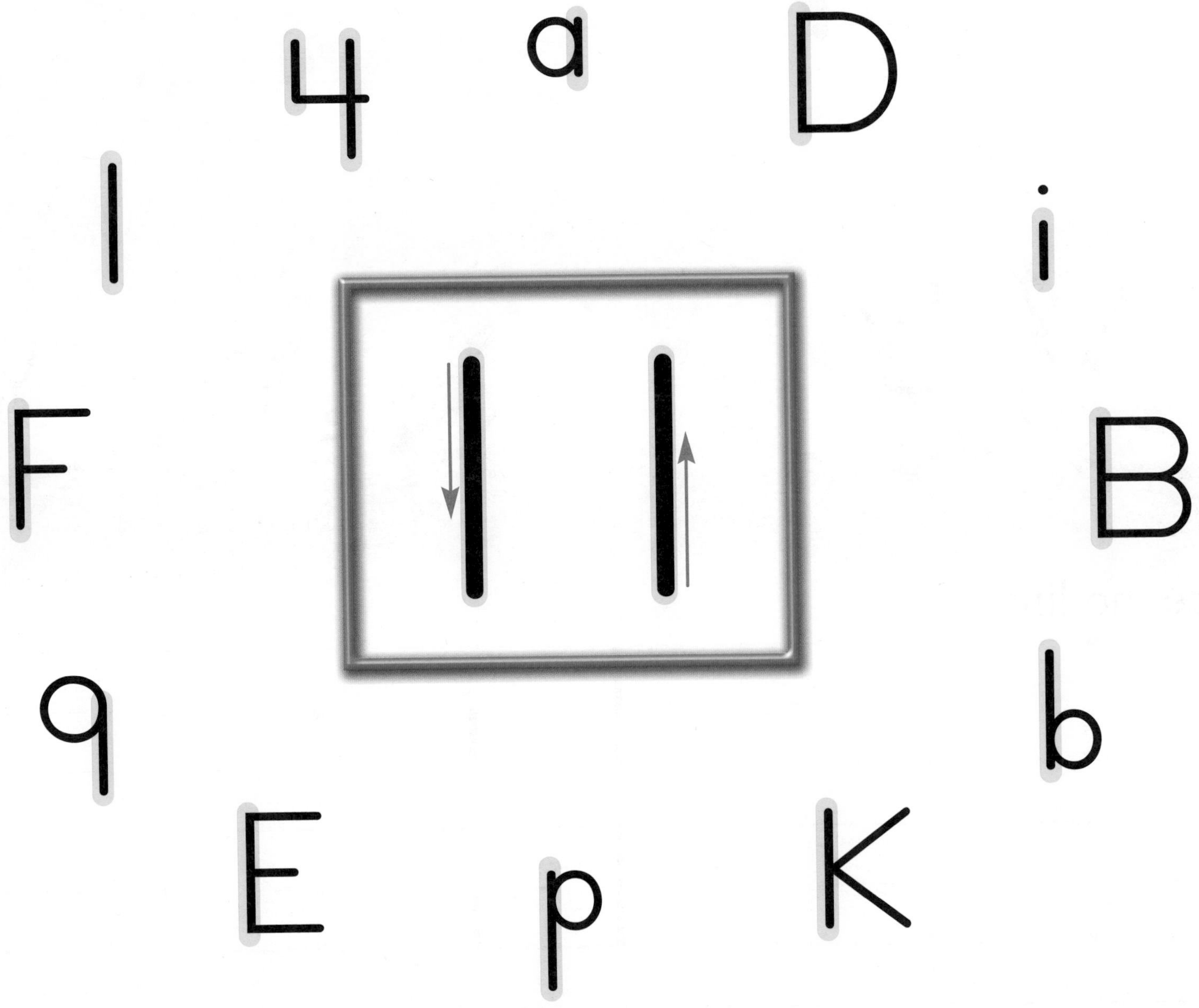

4   a   D

1   i

F   B

q   b

E   p   K

Horizontal Lines

You use horizontal lines when you write.
Place your horizontal strokes below.
Trace them with your finger.

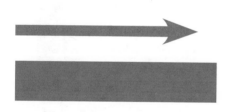

Find horizontal lines in the picture above.
Draw this picture or one of your own.

21

Write horizontal lines.
Start at the ●. Stop at the ●.

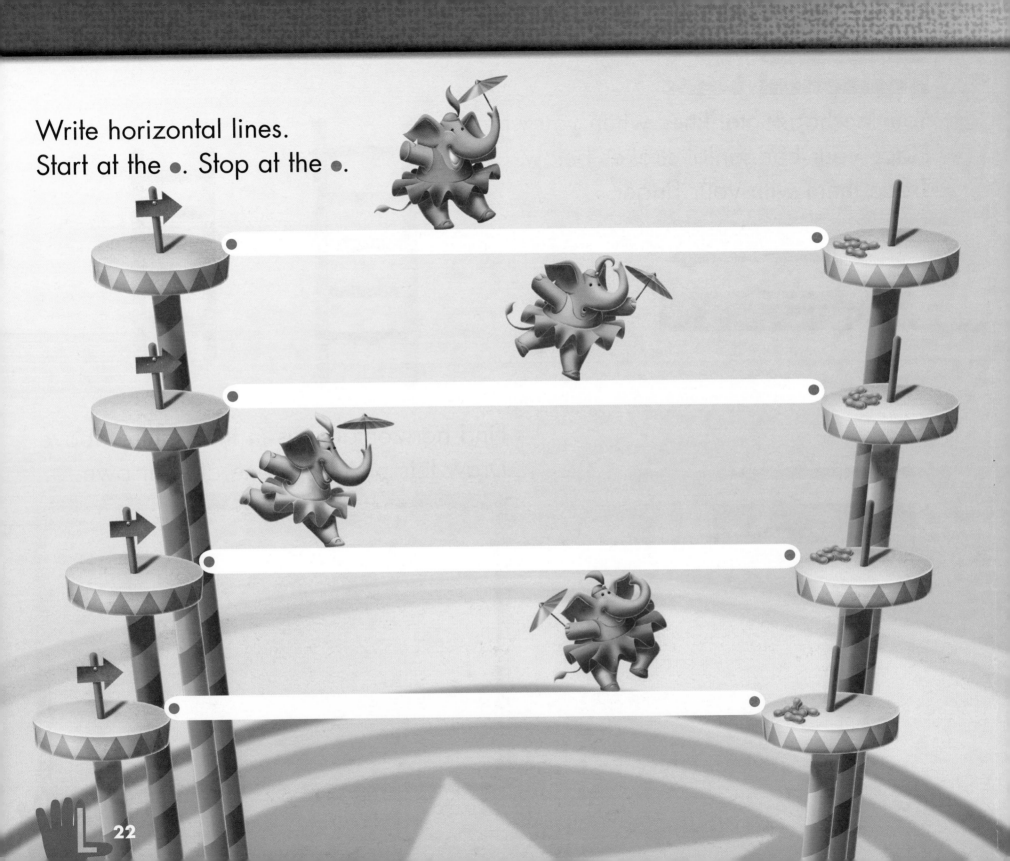

Horizontal Lines

Write horizontal lines.
Start at the ●. Stop at the ●.

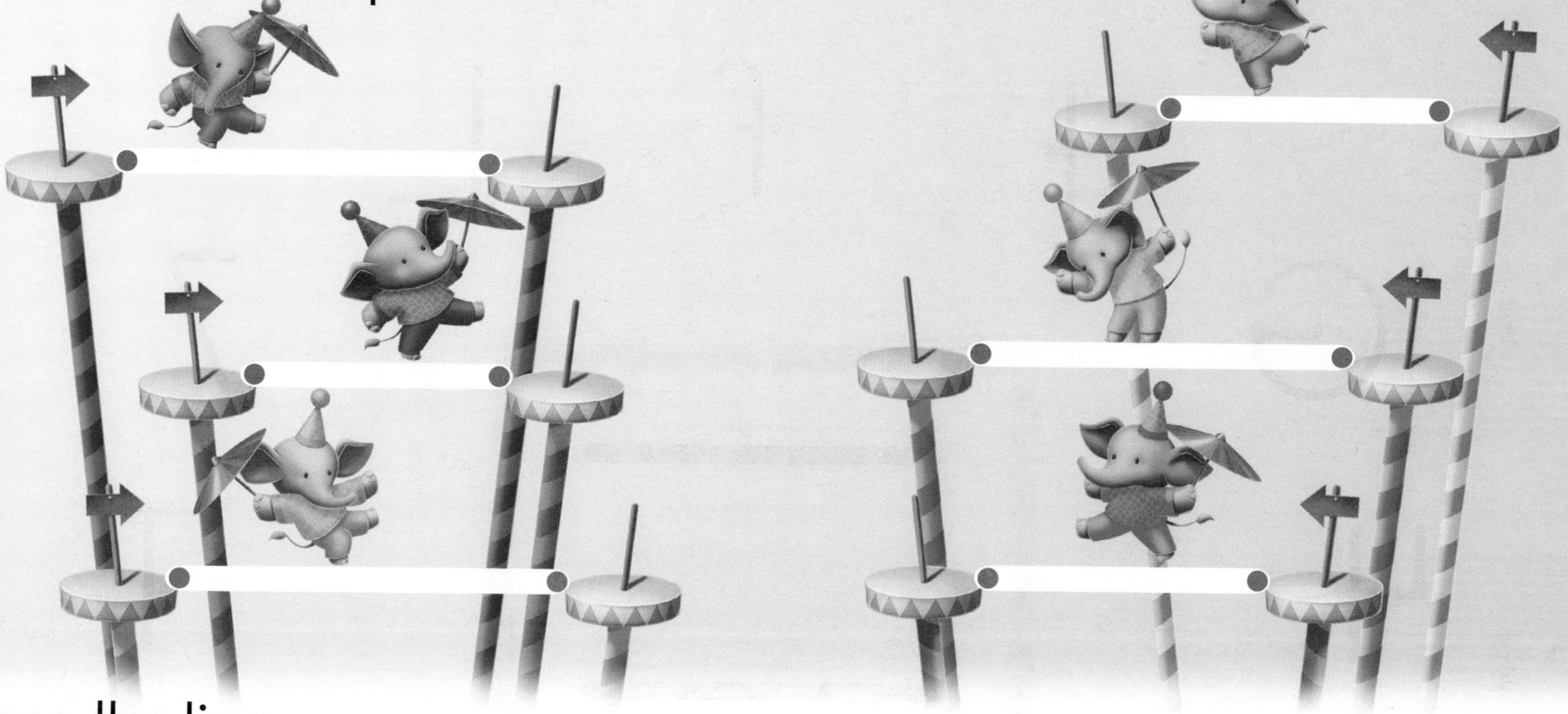

Trace the lines.

Use your finger to trace the horizontal lines
in the letters and numerals.

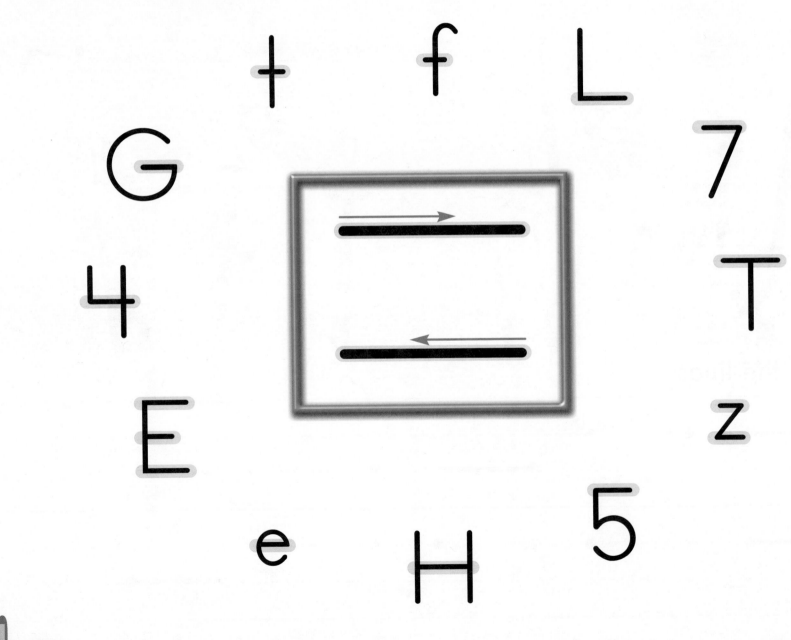

Backward Circle Lines

You use backward circle lines when you write.
Place your circle strokes below.
Trace them with your finger.

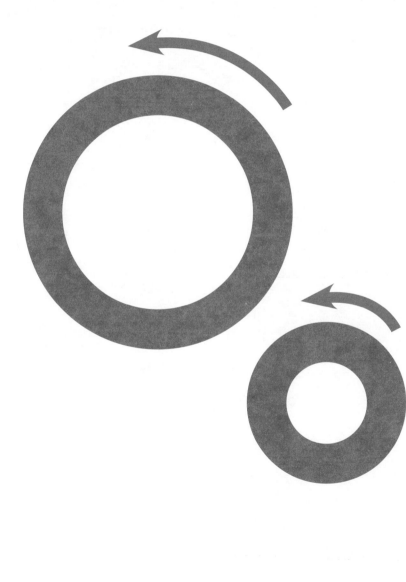

Find circle lines in the picture above.
Draw this picture or one of your own.

Write backward circle lines.
Start at the •. Stop at the •.

Backward Circle Lines

Write backward circle lines.
Start at the •. Stop at the •.

Trace the lines.

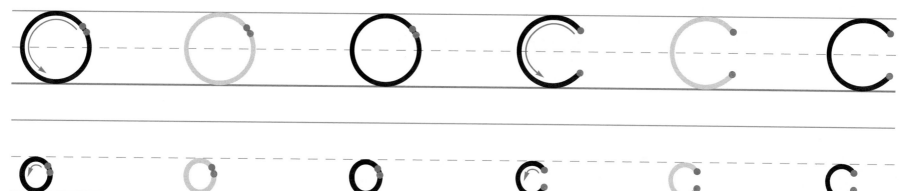

Use your finger to trace the backward circle lines
in the letters and numerals.

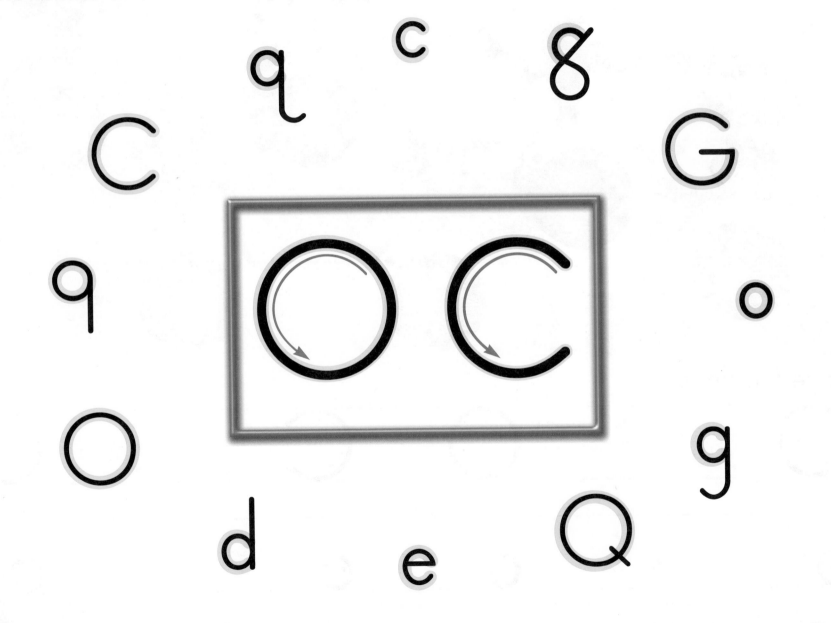

Slant Lines

You use slant lines when you write.
Place your slant strokes below.
Trace them with your finger.

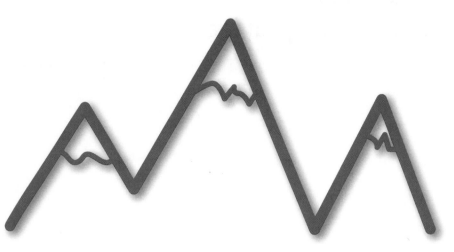

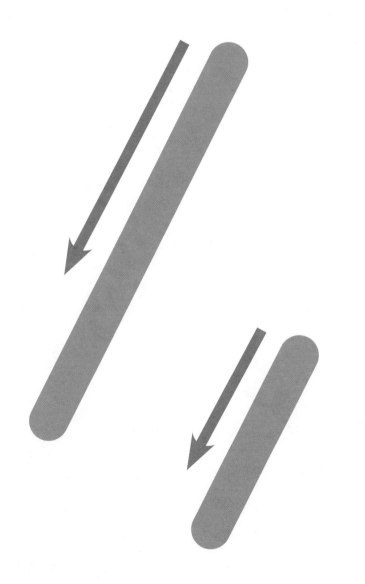

Find slant lines in the picture above.
Draw this picture or one of your own.

29

Write slant lines.
Start at the ●. Stop at the ●.

Slant Lines

Write slant lines.

Start at the ●. Stop at the ●.

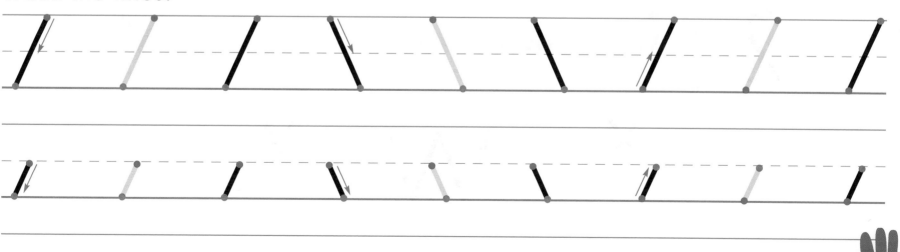

Trace the lines.

Use your finger to trace the slant lines
in the letters and numerals.

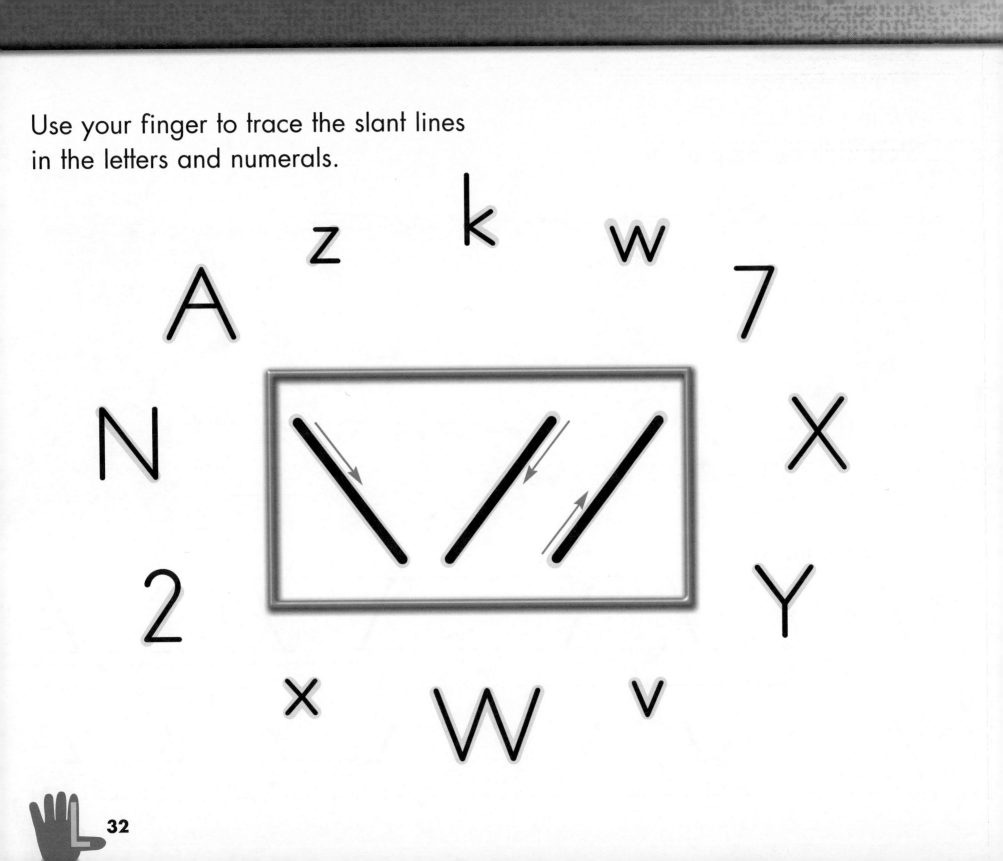

Forward Circle Lines

You use forward circle lines when you write.
Place your circle strokes below.
Trace them with your finger.

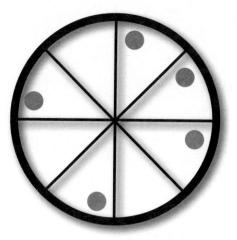

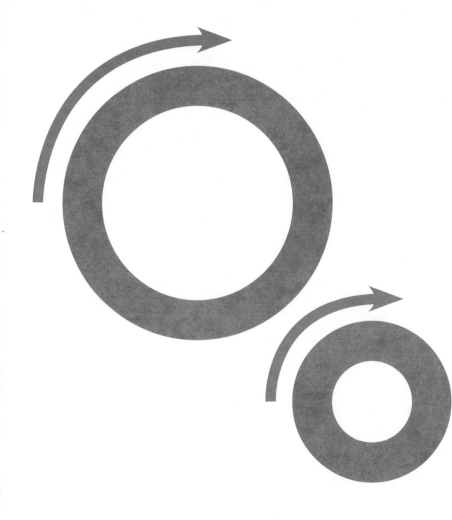

Find circle lines in the picture above.
Draw this picture or one of your own.

33

Write forward circle lines.
Start at the •. Stop at the •.

Forward Circle Lines

Write forward circle lines.
Start at the ●. Stop at the ●.

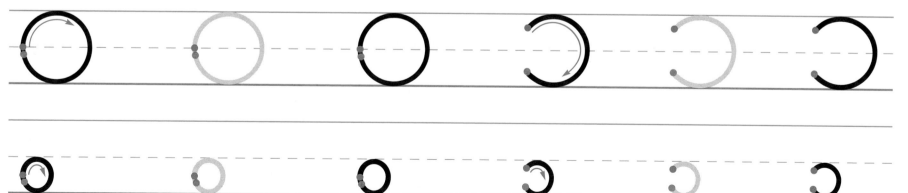

Trace the lines.

Use your finger to trace the forward circle lines
in the letters and numerals.

p D 8

B s

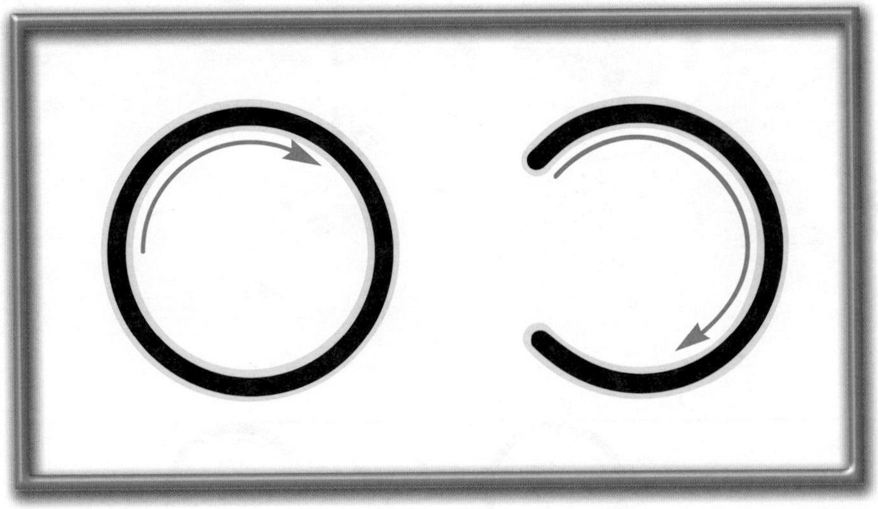

5 b

R 2

S P

3

Four Kinds of Lines

Use the basic strokes to draw the window frames.

Use the basic strokes to draw a line around each window.

Dogs

The dogs I know
Have many shapes.
For some are big and tall,

And some are long,

And
Some
Are thin,

And some are fat and small.

And some are little bits of fluff
And have no shape at all.

Marchette Gaylord Chute

Help the dog find its owner.

Lemonade

Trace and write.

L L L L L L L ✓

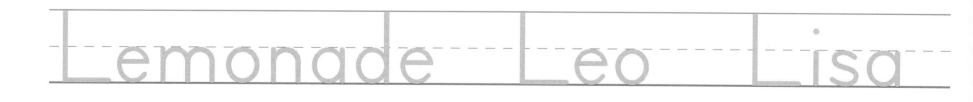

Lemonade Leo Lisa

Directions:

Discuss the picture on the page. Help students identify **L** in the word on the sign.

Stroke description to guide letter formation at home:

l. Pull down straight. Slide right.

41

lion

leaf

lemon

Lemonade

Trace and write.

lion   leaf   lemon

Stroke description to guide letter formation at home:

l. Pull down straight.

42

Insect Island

Trace and write.

Insect Island   Ian

Directions:

Discuss the picture on the page. Help students identify **I** in the words on the banner.

Stroke description to guide letter formation at home:

I. Pull down straight. Lift.
2. Slide right. Lift.
3. Slide right.

43

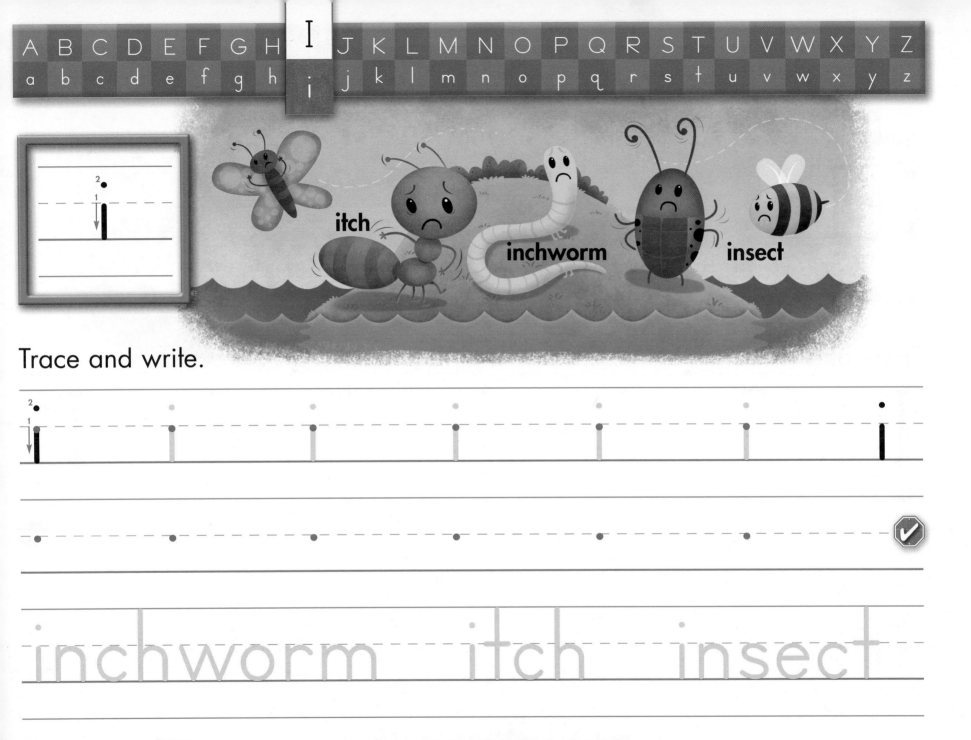

itch

inchworm

insect

Trace and write.

inchworm itch insect

Directions:

Discuss the picture on the page. Help students identify **i** in the words that name the pictures.

Stroke description to guide letter formation at home:

1. Pull down straight. Lift.

2. Dot.

Toot! Toot!

Tiny Town

Trace and write.

Toot!   Tiny Town

Directions:

Discuss the picture on the page. Help students identify **T** in the words in the picture.

Stroke description to guide letter formation at home:

1. Pull down straight. Lift.
2. Slide right.

45

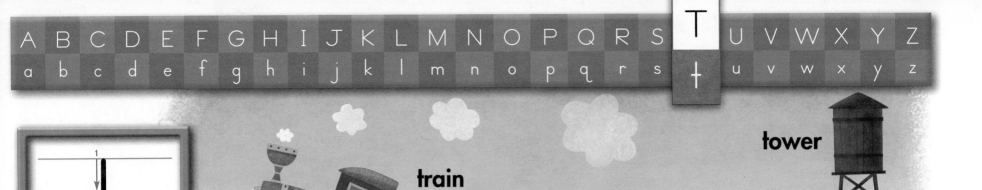

tower

train

track

Trace and write.

train tower track

Directions:

Discuss the picture on the page. Help students identify **t** in the words that name the pictures.

Stroke description to guide letter formation at home:

1. Pull down straight. Lift.
2. Slide right.

46

Write the letters.

l l

i i

t t

L L

I I

T T

47

Write the Alphabet

Write the missing uppercase letters.

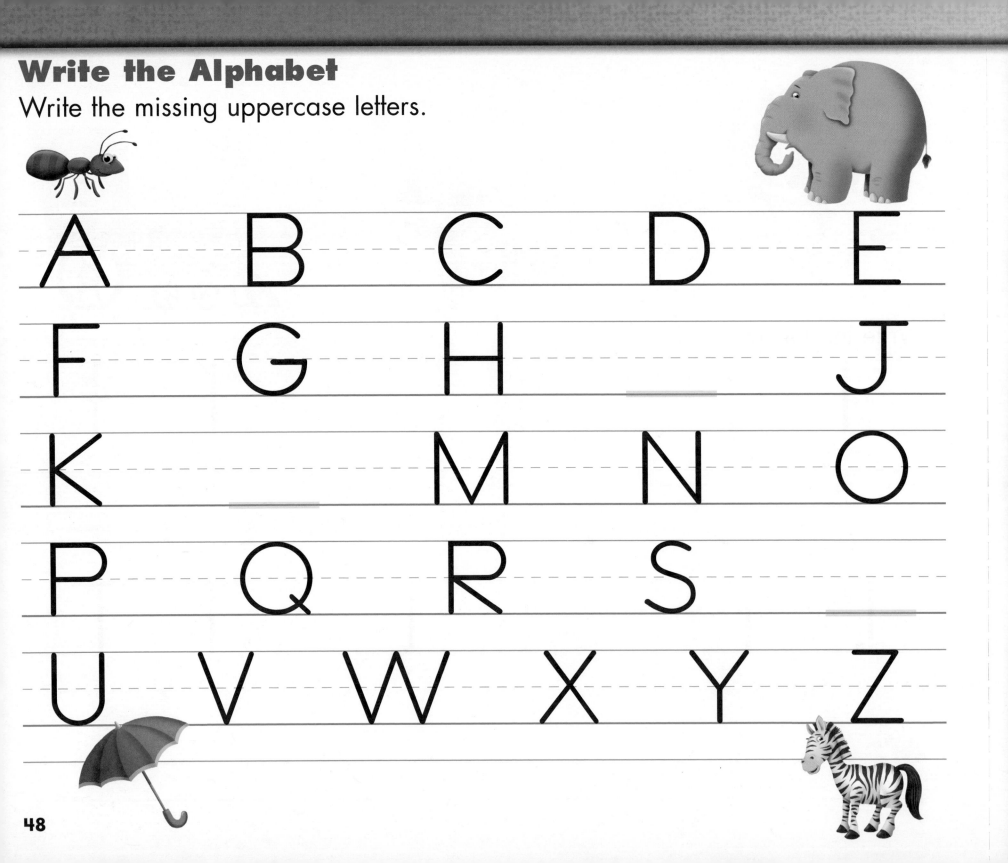

A B C D E

F G H ___ J

K ___ M N O

P Q R S ___

U V W X Y Z

| A B C D E F G H I J K L M N O P Q R S T U V W X Y Z |
| a b c d e f g h i j k l m n o p q r s t u v w x y z |

O
o

Trace and write.

O O O O O O O

On Off Olivia

Directions:

Discuss the picture on the page. Help students identify **O** in the words in the picture.

Stroke description to guide letter formation at home:

I. Circle back all the way around.

49

owl

open

octopus

On Off

Trace and write.

O   O   O   O   O   O   O

octopus   owl   open

School Home

Directions:

Discuss the picture on the page. Help students identify **o** in the words that name the pictures.

Stroke description to guide letter formation at home:

I. Circle back all the way around.

A B C D E F G H I J K L M N O P Q R S T U V W X Y Z
a b c d e f g h i j k l m n o p q r s t u v w x y z

Avenue A

Trace and write.

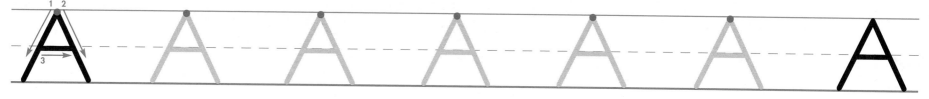

A A A A A A A A A

Avenue   Alex   Abby

Directions:

Discuss the picture on the page. Help students identify **A** in the words on the sign.

Stroke description to guide letter formation at home:

1. Slant left. Lift.
2. Slant right. Lift.
3. Slide right.

51

A

| A | B | C | D | E | F | G | H | I | J | K | L | M | N | O | P | Q | R | S | T | U | V | W | X | Y | Z |
| a | b | c | d | e | f | g | h | i | j | k | l | m | n | o | p | q | r | s | t | u | v | w | x | y | z |

a

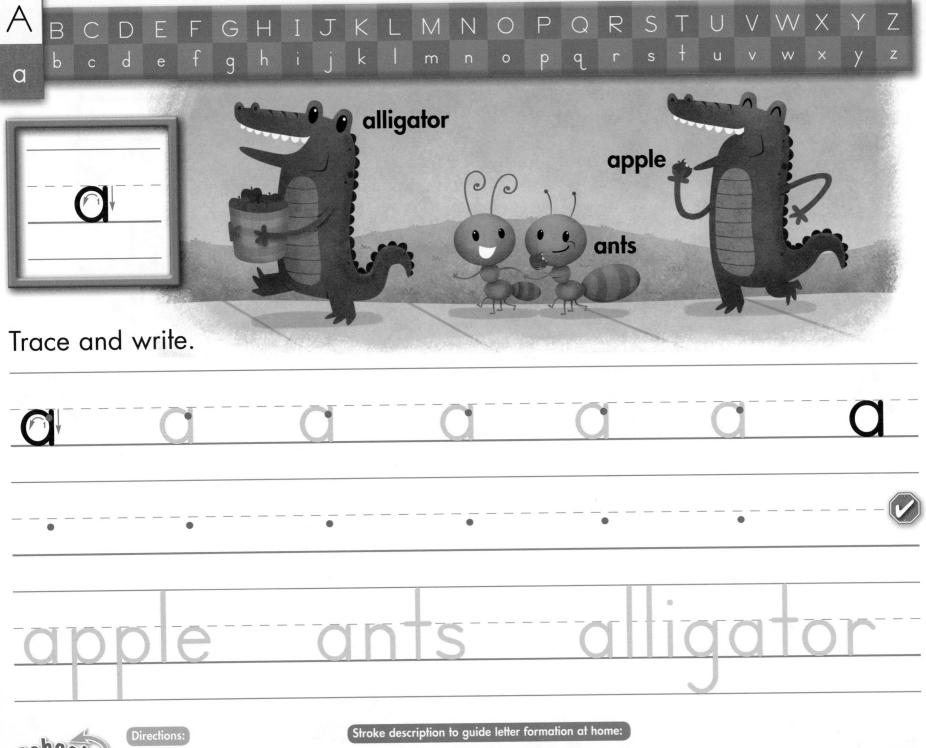

alligator

apple

ants

Trace and write.

a   a   a   a   a   a   a

apple   ants   alligator

school Home

Directions:

Discuss the picture on the page.
Help students identify **a** in the
words that name the pictures.

Stroke description to guide letter formation at home:

I. Circle back all the way around; push up
straight. Pull down straight.

Trace and write.

D D D D D D D D

Don't David Dana

Directions:

Discuss the picture on the page. Help students identify **D** in the words on the sign.

Stroke description to guide letter formation at home:

1. Pull down straight. Lift.
2. Slide right; curve forward; slide left.

53

A B C D E F G H I J K L M N O P Q R S T U V W X Y Z
a b c d e f g h i j k l m n o p q r s t u v w x y z

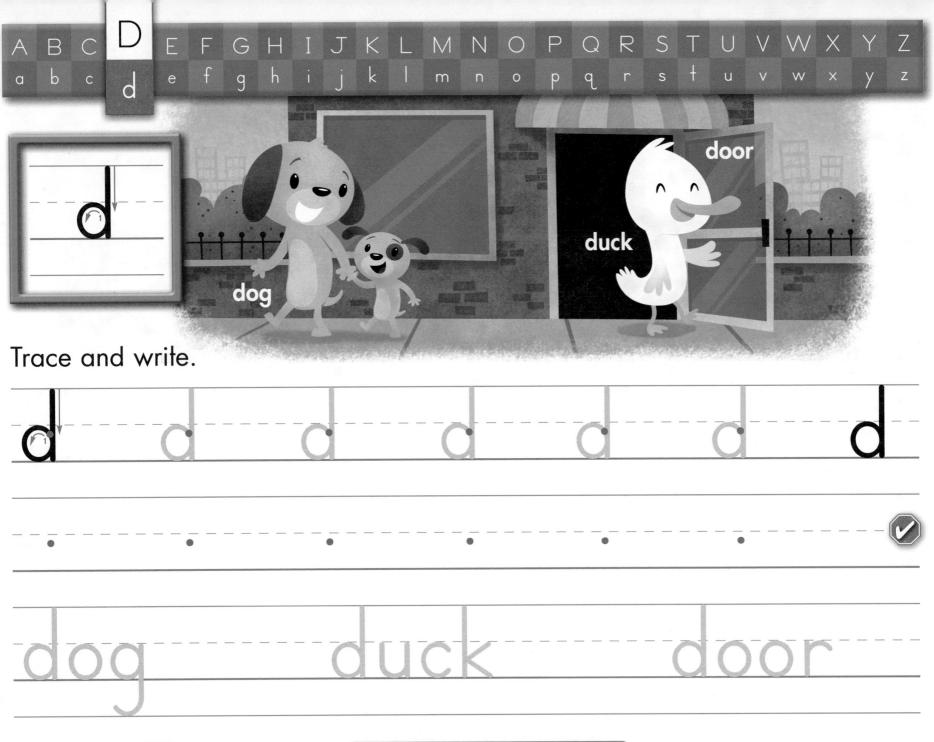

duck

door

dog

Trace and write.

d d d d d d d

dog   duck   door

Directions:

Discuss the picture on the page. Help students identify **d** in the words that name the pictures.

Stroke description to guide letter formation at home:

d   **I.** Circle back all the way around; push up straight. Pull down straight.

54

Write the letters.

o o o

a a a

d d d

O O O

A A A

D D D

55

Write the Alphabet

Write the missing lowercase letters.

b   c   e

f   g   h   j

k   m   n

p   q   r   s

u   v   w   x   y   z

c

Camel's
Cakes

Trace and write.

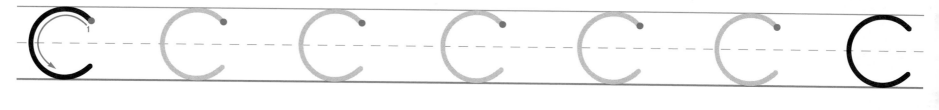

C C C C C C C

Cakes   Cody   Cara

School
Home

Directions:

Discuss the picture on the page.
Help students identify **C** in the
words on the sign.

Stroke description to guide letter formation at home:

C   **I.** Circle back.

A B C D E F G H I J K L M N O P Q R S T U V W X Y Z
a b c d e f g h i j k l m n o p q r s t u v w x y z

C

cook

camel

cup

Trace and write.

C C C C C C C C C

camel   cook   cup

School Home

58

Directions:

Discuss the picture on the page. Help students identify **c** in the words that name the pictures.

Stroke description to guide letter formation at home:

1. Circle back.

C

Trace and write.

E E E E E E E E E

Eye   Eric   Ella

School Home

Directions:

Discuss the picture on the page. Help students identify **E** in the words on the signs.

Stroke description to guide letter formation at home:

E

1. Pull down straight. Lift.
2. Slide right. Lift.
3. Slide right; stop short. Lift.
4. Slide right.

59

| A | B | C | D | **E** | F | G | H | I | J | K | L | M | N | O | P | Q | R | S | T | U | V | W | X | Y | Z |
| a | b | c | d | **e** | f | g | h | i | j | k | l | m | n | o | p | q | r | s | t | u | v | w | x | y | z |

elephant

elk

ear

Trace and write.

e   e   e   e   e   e

elephant   elk   ear

School Home

Directions:

Discuss the picture on the page. Help students identify **e** in the words that name the pictures.

Stroke description to guide letter formation at home:

e

1. Slide right. Circle back.

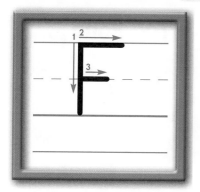

Frog Pond

Trace and write.

F F F F F F F F

Frog Finn Farrah

Directions:
Discuss the picture on the page. Help students identify **F** in the words on the sign.

Stroke description to guide letter formation at home:

1. Pull down straight. Lift.
2. Slide right. Lift.
3. Slide right; stop short.

fly

Frog Pond

flute

fish

Trace and write.

f f f f f f f

flute fish fly

Directions:

Discuss the picture on the page. Help students identify **f** in the words that name the pictures.

Stroke description to guide letter formation at home:

f

1. Curve back; pull down straight. Lift.
2. Slide right.

Write the letters.

c c

e e

f f

C C

E E

F F

Write the Alphabet

Write the missing uppercase letters.

B

B G H J

K M N

P Q R S

U V W X Y Z

Trace and write.

Good night.

G G G G G G G

Good   Gwen   Gabe

Directions:

Discuss the picture on the page. Help students identify **G** in the words in the picture.

Stroke description to guide letter formation at home:

G **1.** Circle back. Slide left.

65

guitar

goat

garden

Trace and write.

g   g   g   g   g   g   g   g

goat   guitar   garden

School Home

Directions:

Discuss the picture on the page. Help students identify **g** in the words that name the pictures.

Stroke description to guide letter formation at home:

I. Circle back all the way around; push up straight. Pull down straight; curve back.

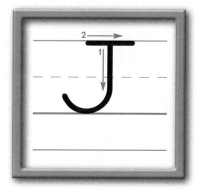

Jay's

Trace and write.

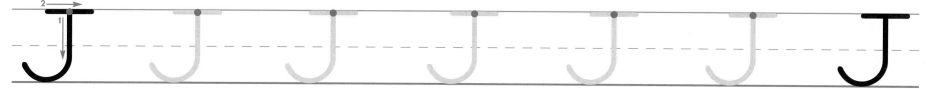

J J J J J J J J J

Jack   Jill   Jay

Directions:

Discuss the picture on the page. Help students identify **J** in the word on the sign.

Stroke description to guide letter formation at home:

1. Pull down straight; curve back. Lift.
2. Slide right.

67

juice

jar

jam

Trace and write.

j   j   j   j   j   j   j   j

jam   juice   jar

Directions:

Discuss the picture on the page. Help students identify **j** in the words that name the pictures.

Stroke description to guide letter formation at home:

1. Pull down straight; curve back. Lift.
2. Dot.

68

Quiet!

Quack!
Quack!

Trace and write.

Q Q Q Q Q Q Q

Quiet! Quack! Quinn

School
Home

Directions:

Discuss the picture on the page. Help students identify **Q** in the words in the picture.

Stroke description to guide letter formation at home:

1. Circle back all the way around. Lift.
2. Slant right.

69

A B C D E F G H I J K L M N O P **Q** R S T U V W X Y Z

a b c d e f g h i j k l m n o p **q** r s t u v w x y z

queen

quail

quilt

Trace and write.

q q q q q q q

queen   quail   quilt

School Home

70

Directions:

Discuss the picture on the page. Help students identify **q** in the words that name the pictures.

Stroke description to guide letter formation at home:

I. Circle back all the way around; push up straight. Pull down straight; curve forward.

Write the letters.

g   g

j   j

q   q

G   G

J   J

Q   Q

Write the Alphabet

Write the missing lowercase letters.

b

   h

k   m n

p   r s

u v w x y z

Upside-down Town

Trace and write.

U U U U U U U

Upside   Uma   Uri

School Home

Directions:
Discuss the picture on the page. Help students identify **U** in the words on the sign.

Stroke description to guide letter formation at home:

1. Pull down straight; curve forward; push up.

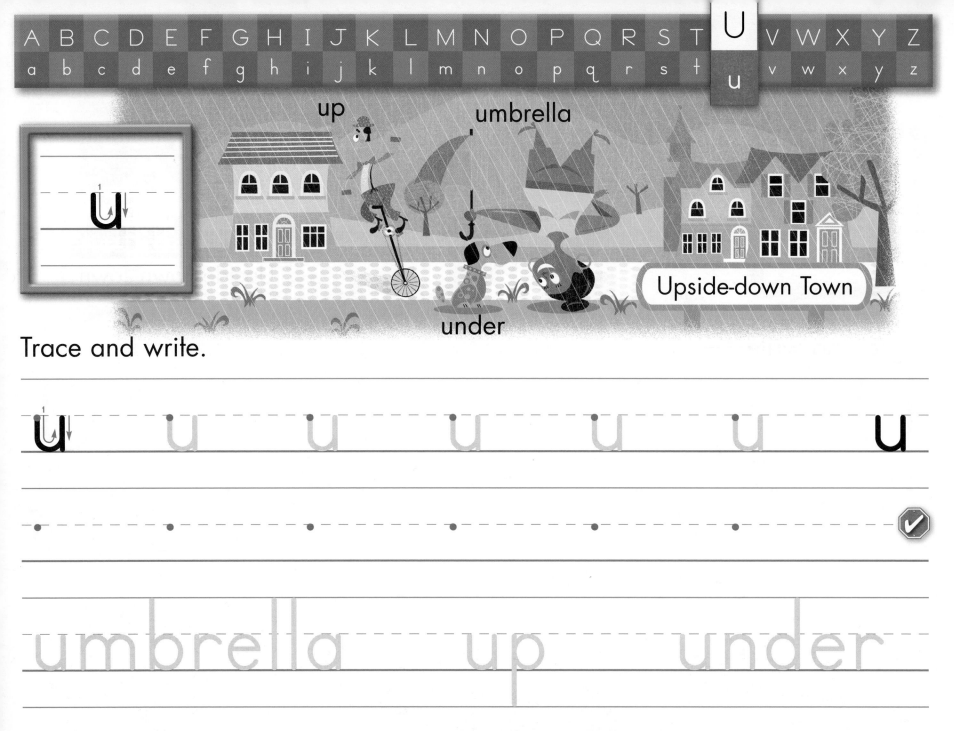

up

umbrella

Upside-down Town

under

Trace and write.

u u u u u u u

umbrella up under

school Home

Directions:
Discuss the picture on the page. Help students identify **u** in the words that name the pictures.

Stroke description to guide letter formation at home:

I. Pull down straight; curve forward; push up. Pull down straight.

S

Trace and write.

S   S   S   S   S   S

Stop   School Street

School Home

Directions:
Discuss the picture on the page. Help students identify **S** in the words on the signs.

Stroke description to guide letter formation at home:

S   **I.** Curve back; curve forward.

75

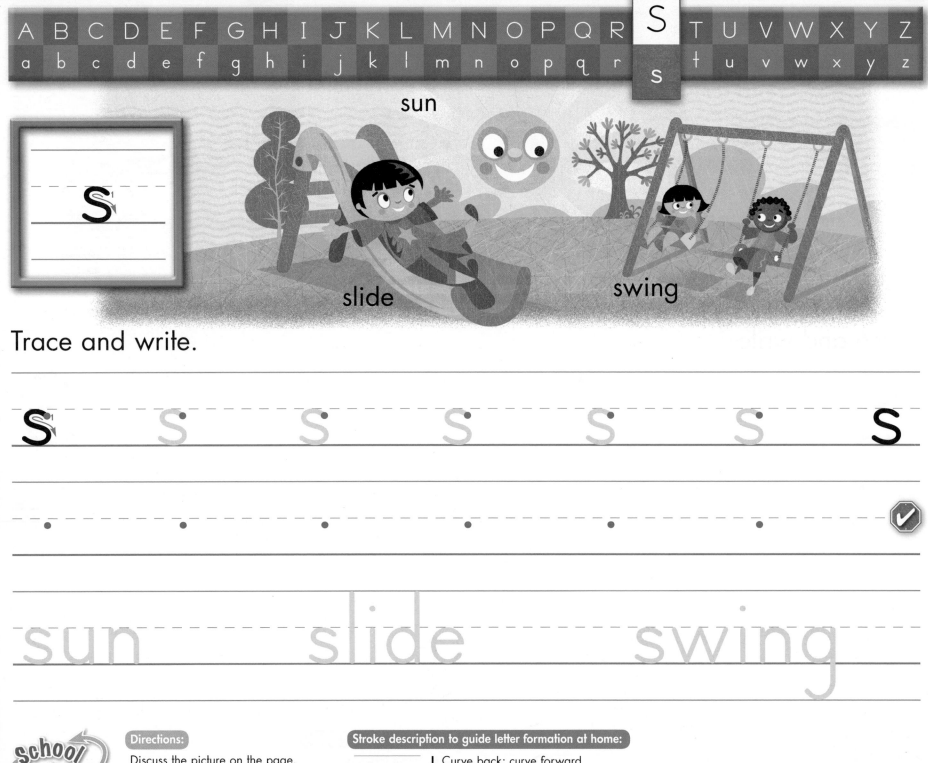

sun

slide

swing

Trace and write.

S s s s s s s

sun   slide   swing

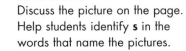

Directions:

Discuss the picture on the page. Help students identify **s** in the words that name the pictures.

Stroke description to guide letter formation at home:

I. Curve back; curve forward.

Baby Bear's Balloons

Trace and write.

Baby Bear   Ben

School Home

Directions:

Discuss the picture on the page. Help students identify **B** in the words on the sign.

Stroke description to guide letter formation at home:

B

1. Pull down straight. Lift.
2. Slide right; curve forward; slide left. Slide right; curve forward; slide left.

77

bear

balloon

bird

Baby Bear's Balloons

Trace and write.

b b b b b b b b

bear balloon bird

School Home

Directions:
Discuss the picture on the page.
Help students identify **b** in the
words that name the pictures.

Stroke description to guide letter formation at home:

1. Pull down straight.
   Push up; circle forward.

P
p

Pet Store

Peter

Trace and write.

Pet   Pam   Peter

Directions:
Discuss the picture on the page. Help students identify **P** in the words on the signs.

Stroke description to guide letter formation at home:
P
1. Pull down straight. Lift.
2. Slide right; curve forward; slide left.

A B C D E F G H I J K L M N O P Q R S T U V W X Y Z
a b c d e f g h i j k l m n o p q r s t u v w x y z

parrot

pig

Peter

poodle

Pet Store

Trace and write.

p   p   p   p   p   p   p   p   p

pig   parrot   poodle

School Home

Stroke description to guide letter formation at home:

p

l. Pull down straight. Push up; circle forward.

Write the letters.

u u s s b b p p

U U S S B B P P

Write the Alphabet

Write the missing uppercase letters.

H

K   M   N

R

V W X Y Z

Rowboat Rides

Trace and write.

R R R R R R R R

Rides   Rob   Rachel

School Home

Directions:

Discuss the picture on the page. Help students identify **R** in the words on the sign.

Stroke description to guide letter formation at home:

1. Pull down straight. Lift.
2. Slide right; curve forward; slide left. Slant right.

83

rowboat rabbit red

Trace and write.

r r r r r r r

rabbit   red   rowboat

School Home

Stroke description to guide letter formation at home:

l. Pull down straight. Push up; curve forward.

r

84

Trace and write.

N N N N N N N N

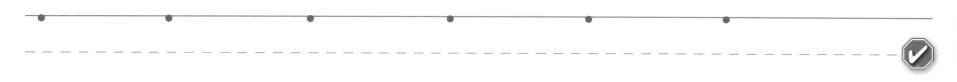

News   Nick   Natalie

Directions:

Discuss the picture on the page. Help students identify **N** in the words on the newspaper.

Stroke description to guide letter formation at home:

N **1.** Pull down straight. Lift.
2. Slant right. Push up straight.

85

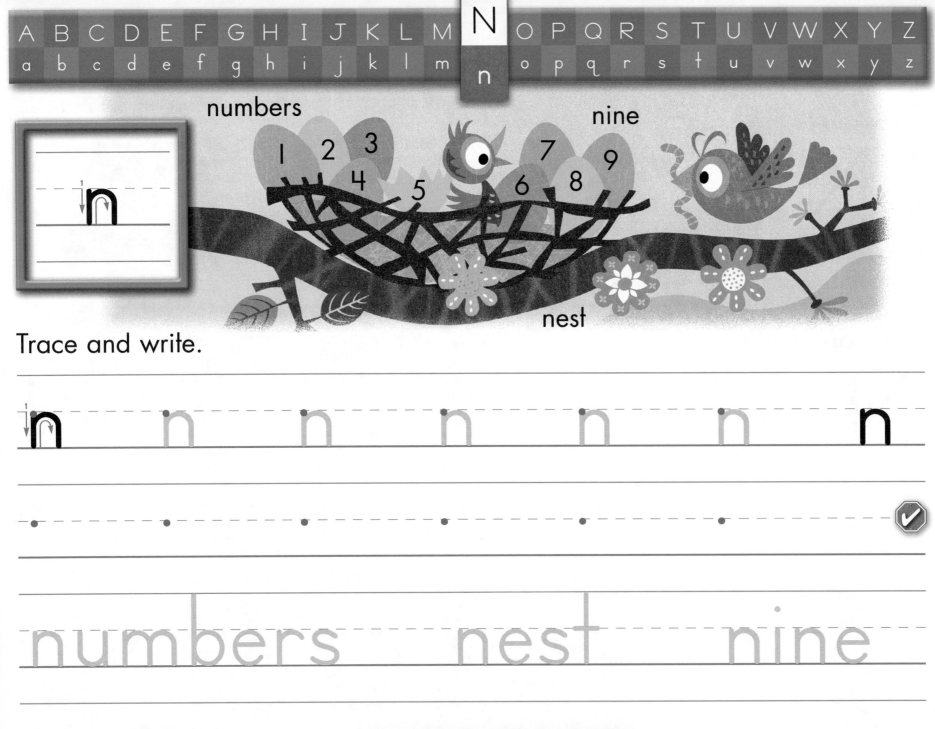

numbers

nine

1 2 3
4 5 6 7 8 9

nest

Trace and write.

n n n n n n n

numbers   nest   nine

School Home

Directions:

Discuss the picture on the page. Help students identify **n** in the words that name the pictures.

Stroke description to guide letter formation at home:

n

l. Pull down straight. Push up; curve forward; pull down straight.

Moo!

Trace and write.

M M M M M M M

Moo! Megan Matt

School Home

Directions:

Discuss the picture on the page. Help students identify **M** in the word in the picture.

Stroke description to guide letter formation at home:

1. Pull down straight. Lift.
2. Slant right. Slant up. Pull down straight.

moon

milk

mouse

Trace and write.

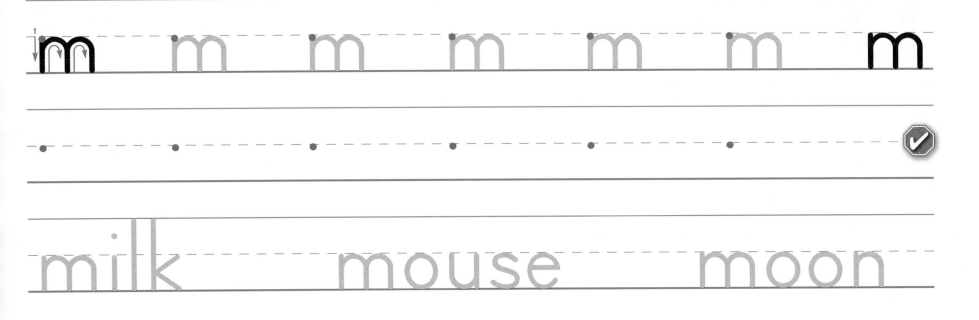

m m m m m m m m

milk   mouse   moon

School Home

Directions:

Discuss the picture on the page. Help students identify **m** in the words that name the pictures.

Stroke description to guide letter formation at home:

l. Pull down straight. Push up; curve forward; pull down straight. Push up; curve forward; pull down straight.

88

Happy Birthday, Helen

Trace and write.

H H H H H H H H H

Helen Hen Happy

Directions:

Discuss the picture on the page. Help students identify **H** in the words on the sign.

Stroke description to guide letter formation at home:

1. Pull down straight. Lift.
2. Pull down straight. Lift.
3. Slide right.

89

hat

hen

hill

Trace and write.

h   h   h   h   h   h   h

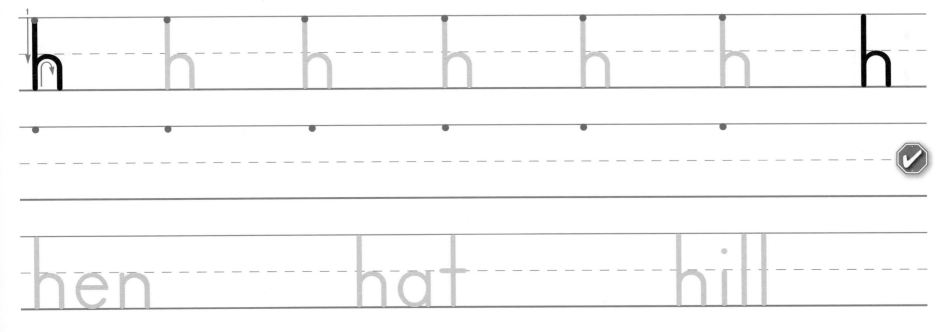

hen   hat   hill

School Home

Directions:

Discuss the picture on the page. Help students identify **h** in the words that name the pictures.

Stroke description to guide letter formation at home:

h **I.** Pull down straight. Push up; curve forward; pull down straight.

90

Write the letters.

r r   n n   m m   h h

R R   N N   M M   H H

Write the Alphabet

Write the missing lowercase letters.

k

v   w   x   y   z

Val's Vans

Moving Van

Trace and write.

V   V   V   V   V   V   V   V   V

Van   Vinny   Val

Directions:

Discuss the picture on the page. Help students identify **V** in the words in the picture.

Stroke description to guide letter formation at home:

V   **I.** Slant right. Slant up.

93

violets

violin

vase

Moving Van

Trace and write.

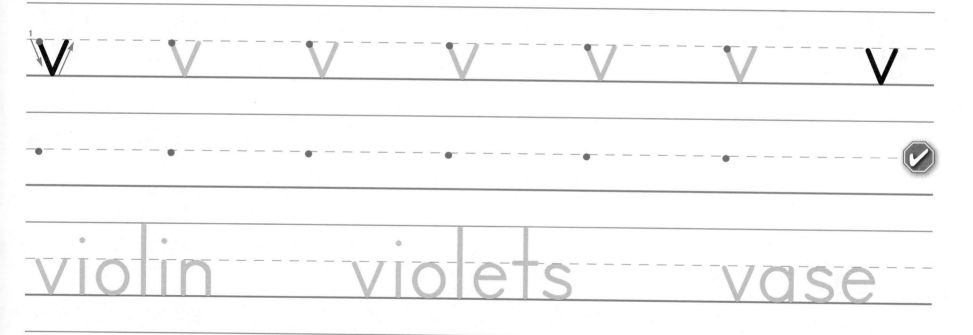

V V V V V V V V V

violin   violets   vase

School Home

Directions:
Discuss the picture on the page. Help students identify **v** in the words that name the pictures.

Stroke description to guide letter formation at home:
1. Slant right. Slant up.

Yard
Sale

Trace and write.

Y Y Y Y Y Y

Yard Yoko Yana

Directions:

Discuss the picture on the page. Help students identify **Y** in the words on the sign.

Stroke description to guide letter formation at home:

1. Slant right. Lift.
2. Slant left. Pull down straight.

95

yellow

yarn

Yard
Sale

yo-yo

Trace and write.

yo-yo   yellow   yarn

School
Home

Directions:

Discuss the picture on the page.
Help students identify **y** in the
words that name the pictures.

Stroke description to guide letter formation at home:

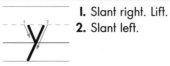

1. Slant right. Lift.

2. Slant left.

Welcome, Walt!

Trace and write.

W W W W W W W W

Welcome, Walt! Will

Directions:

Discuss the picture on the page. Help students identify **W** in the words in the speech bubble.

Stroke description to guide letter formation at home:

I. Slant right. Slant up. Slant right. Slant up.

97

window

wheel

wagon

Trace and write.

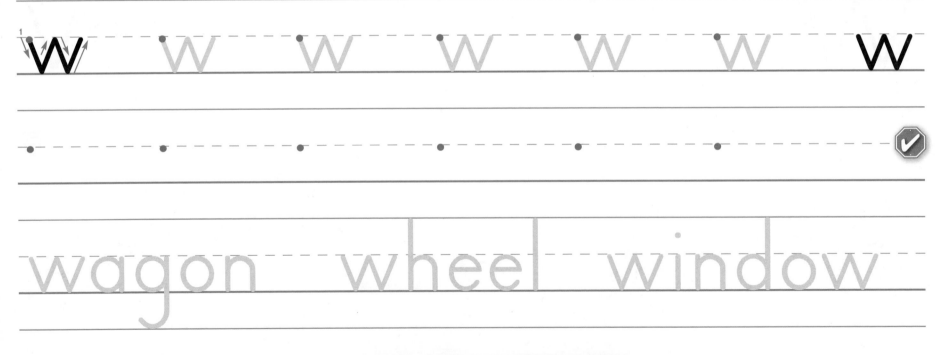

w w w w w w w

wagon wheel window

Stroke description to guide letter formation at home:

I. Slant right. Slant up. Slant right. Slant up.

w

98

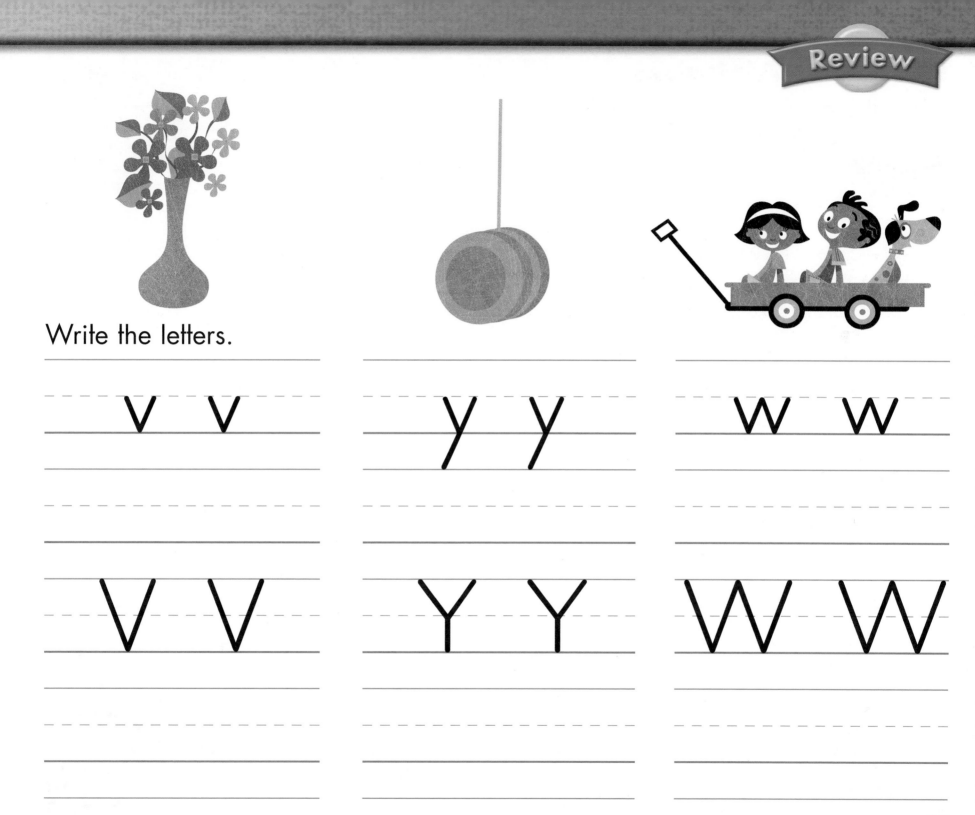

Write the letters.

v v

y y

w w

V V

Y Y

W W

Write the Alphabet

Write the missing uppercase letters.

K

X   Z

EXIT

Trace and write.

X X X X X X X X

EXIT Xavier Xiang

Directions:

Discuss the picture on the page. Help students identify **X** in the word on the sign.

Stroke description to guide letter formation at home:

1. Slant right. Lift.
2. Slant left.

101

A B C D E F G H I J K L M N O P Q R S T U V W X Y Z
a b c d e f g h i j k l m n o p q r s t u v w x y z

fox

box

ox

EXIT

Trace and write.

X X X X X X X X

fox box ox

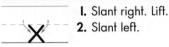 **Directions:**

Discuss the picture on the page. Help students identify **x** in the words that name the pictures.

102

Stroke description to guide letter formation at home:

1. Slant right. Lift.
2. Slant left.

Kate's Kittens

Trace and write.

K K K K K K K

Kittens Kate Kevin

School Home

Directions:

Discuss the picture on the page. Help students identify **K** in the words on the label.

Stroke description to guide letter formation at home:

K **1.** Pull down straight. Lift.
2. Slant left. Slant right.

103

kite

king

key

Trace and write.

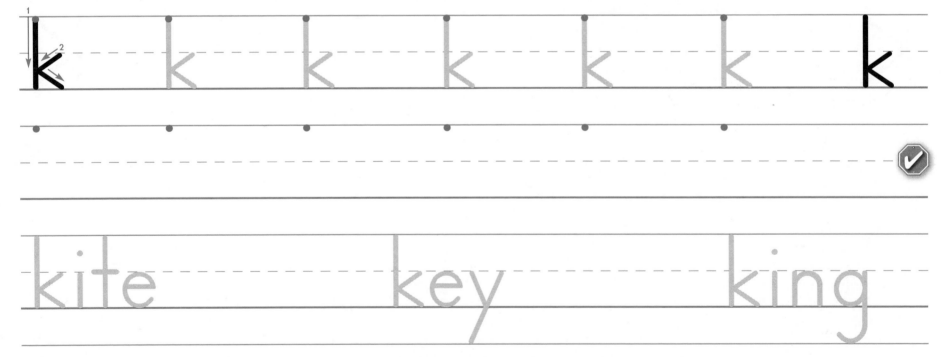

k k k k k k k

kite   key   king

Directions:
Discuss the picture on the page. Help students identify **k** in the words that name the pictures.

Stroke description to guide letter formation at home:

l. Pull down straight. Lift.
2. Slant left. Slant right.

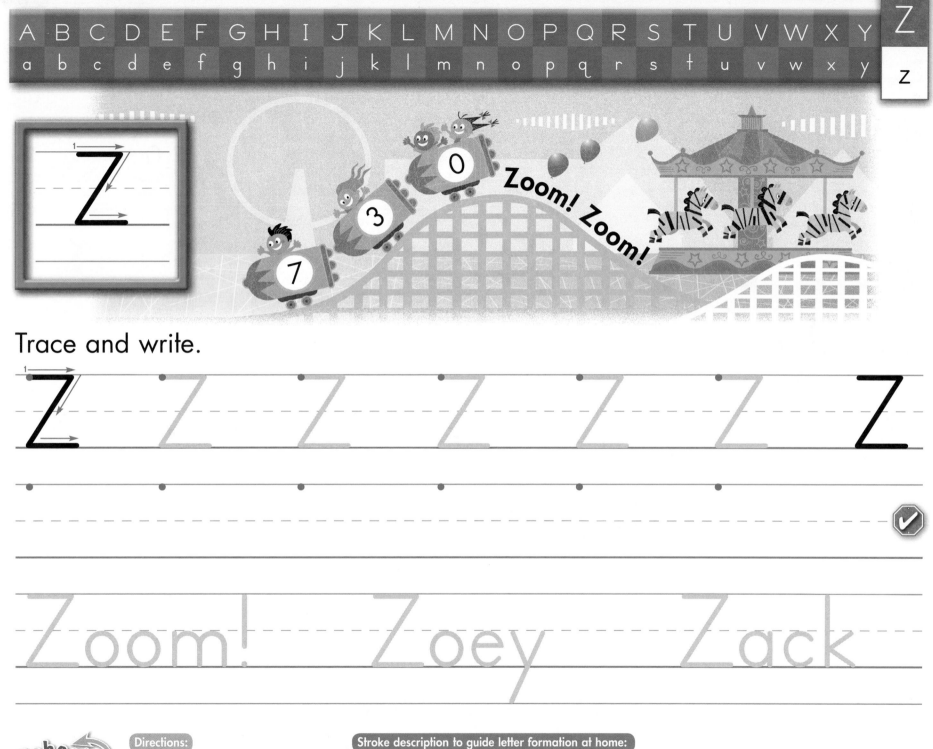

Zoom! Zoom!

Trace and write.

Z Z Z Z Z Z Z Z

Zoom!   Zoey   Zack

Directions:

Discuss the picture on the page. Help students identify **Z** in the words in the picture.

Stroke description to guide letter formation at home:

Z **1.** Slide right. Slant left. Slide right.

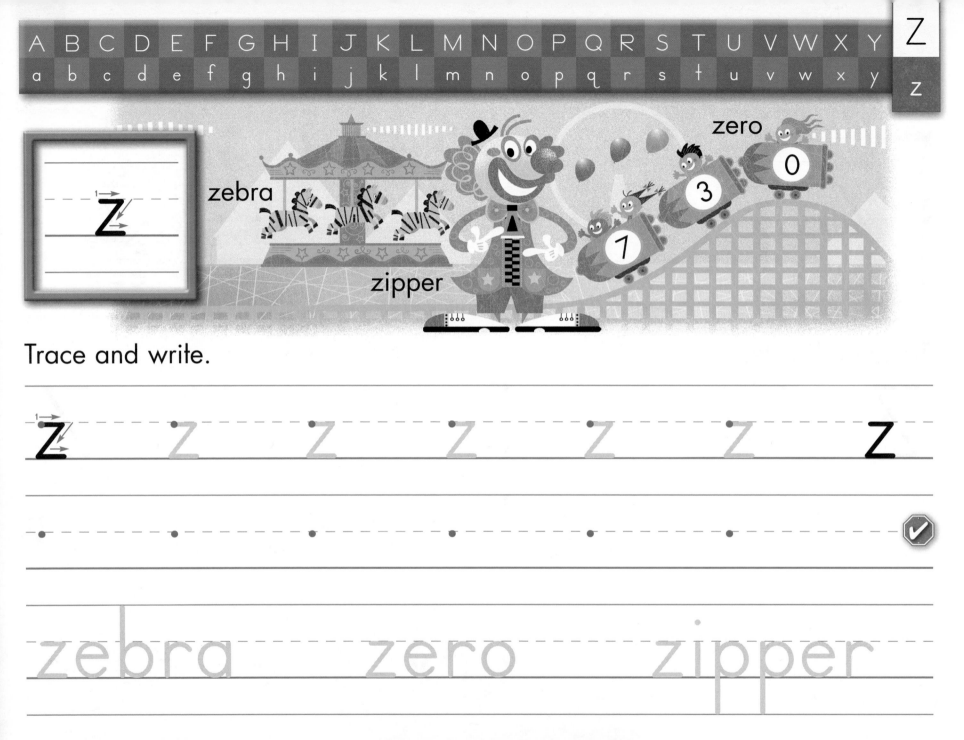

zebra

zipper

zero

7 3 0

Trace and write.

Z Z Z Z Z Z Z Z Z

zebra zero zipper

Directions:

Discuss the picture on the page. Help students identify **z** in the words that name the pictures.

Stroke description to guide letter formation at home:

I. Slide right. Slant left. Slide right.

Z

Write the letters.

x x

k k

z z

X X

K K

Z Z

Write the Alphabet

Write the uppercase alphabet.

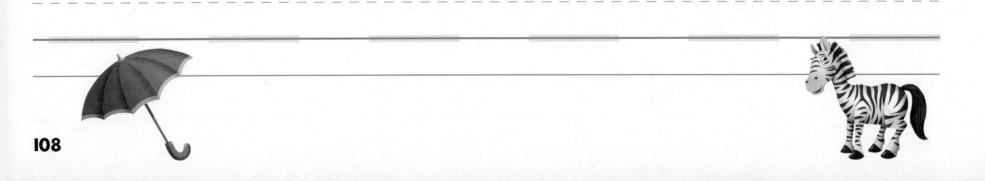

Write the Alphabet

Write the lowercase alphabet.

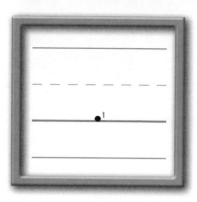

Trace and write.

✓

Run. Pass. Kick.

School Home

Directions:

Discuss the picture on the page. Help students identify things in the shape of a period that are in the picture.

Stroke description to guide punctuation formation at home:

I. Dot.

110

Trace and write.

, , ,

a, b, c   A, B, C

Directions:

Discuss the picture on the page. Help students identify things in the shape of a comma that are in the picture.

Stroke description to guide punctuation formation at home:

1. Dot; curve forward.

,

Write . and , .

. . . . . , , , , ,

Write the sentence.

1, 2, 3, go.

The Clock

With a tick and a tock,
And a tick and a tock,
The clock goes around all day.
It tells us when it's time to work,
And when it's time to play.

Unknown

Follow the maze through the clock.

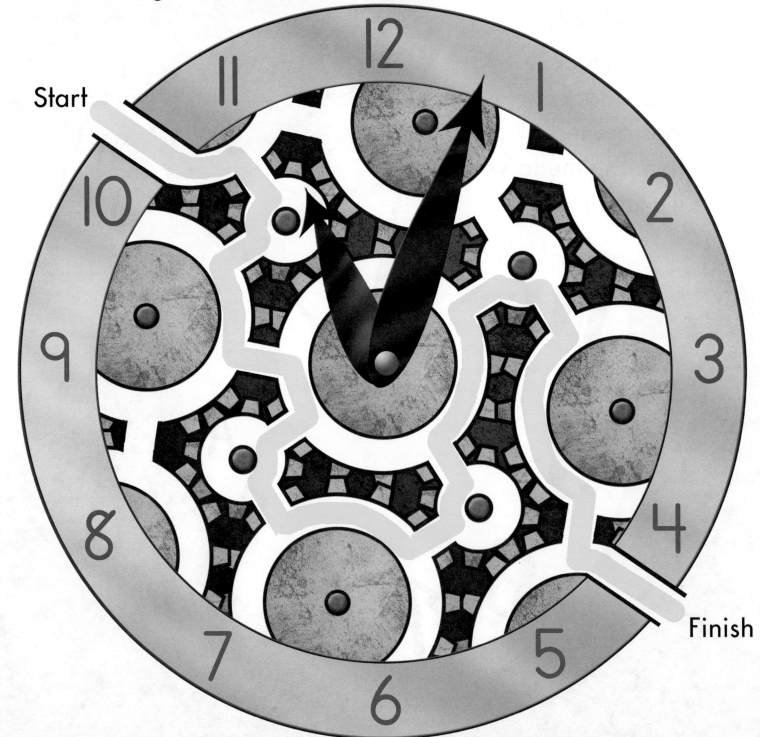

Trace and write.

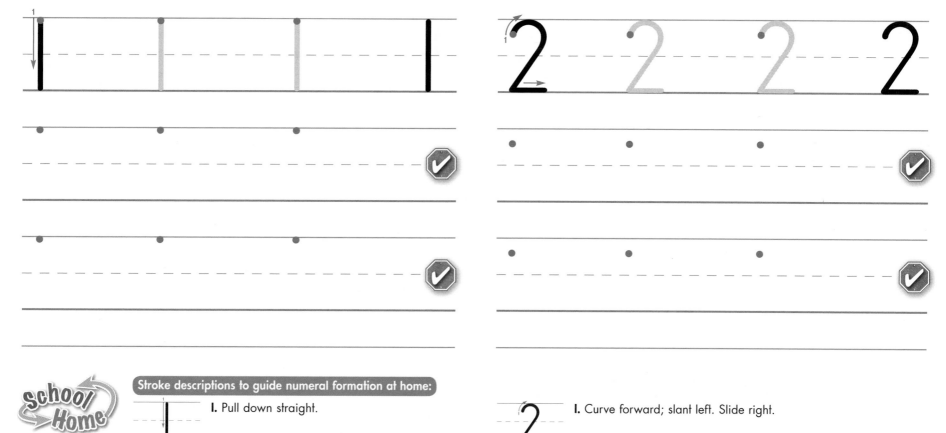

Stroke descriptions to guide numeral formation at home:

1. Pull down straight.

1. Curve forward; slant left. Slide right.

Trace and write.

3 3 3 3

4 4 4 4

Stroke descriptions to guide numeral formation at home:

3 **1.** Curve forward. Curve forward.

4 **1.** Pull down straight. Slide right. Lift.
2. Pull down straight.

Trace and write.

5   5   5   5

6   6   6   6

Stroke descriptions to guide numeral formation at home:

5
1. Pull down straight. Circle forward. Lift.
2. Slide right.

6
1. Curve down; curve up and around.

Trace and write.

7 7 7 7

8 8 8 8

Stroke descriptions to guide numeral formation at home:

7   **I.** Slide right. Slant left.

8   **I.** Curve back; curve forward; slant up.

Trace and write.

9   9   9   9

10   10   10

Stroke descriptions to guide numeral formation at home:

9   **1.** Circle back all the way around.
Pull down straight.

10   **1.** Pull down straight. Lift.
2. Curve down; curve up.

Trace and write.

Stroke descriptions to guide numeral formation at home:

1. Pull down straight. Lift.
2. Pull down straight.

1. Pull down straight. Lift.
2. Curve forward; slant left. Slide right.

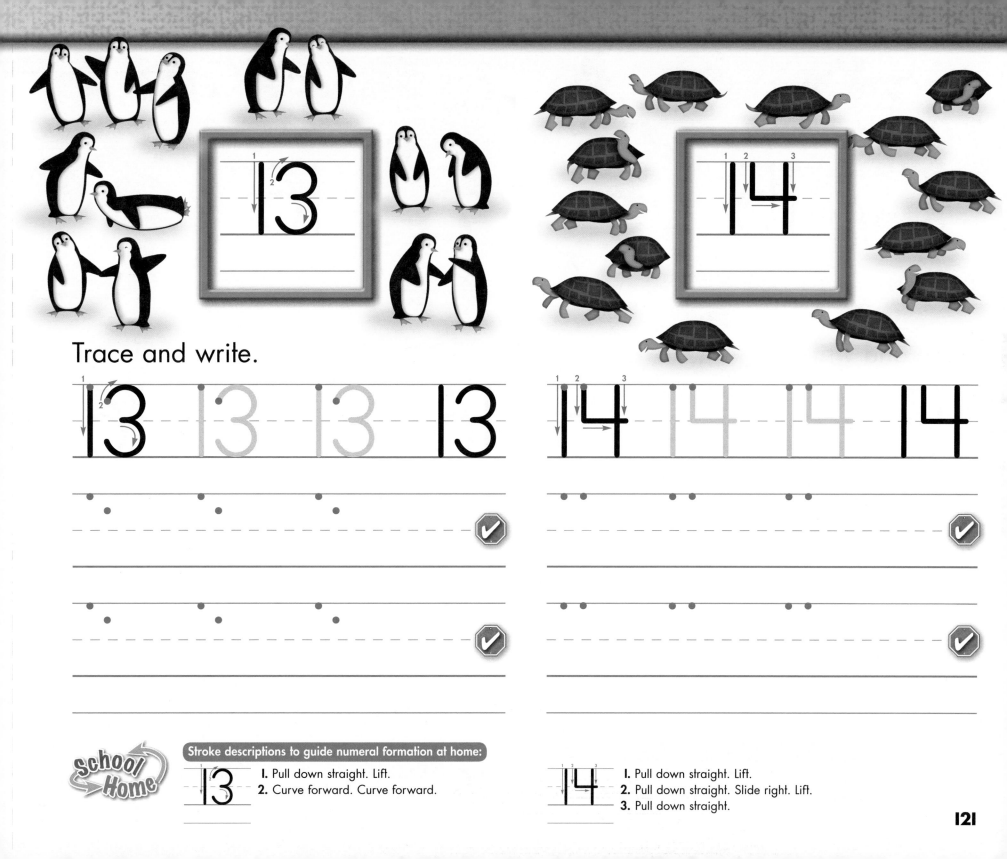

Trace and write.

Stroke descriptions to guide numeral formation at home:

13
1. Pull down straight. Lift.
2. Curve forward. Curve forward.

14
1. Pull down straight. Lift.
2. Pull down straight. Slide right. Lift.
3. Pull down straight.

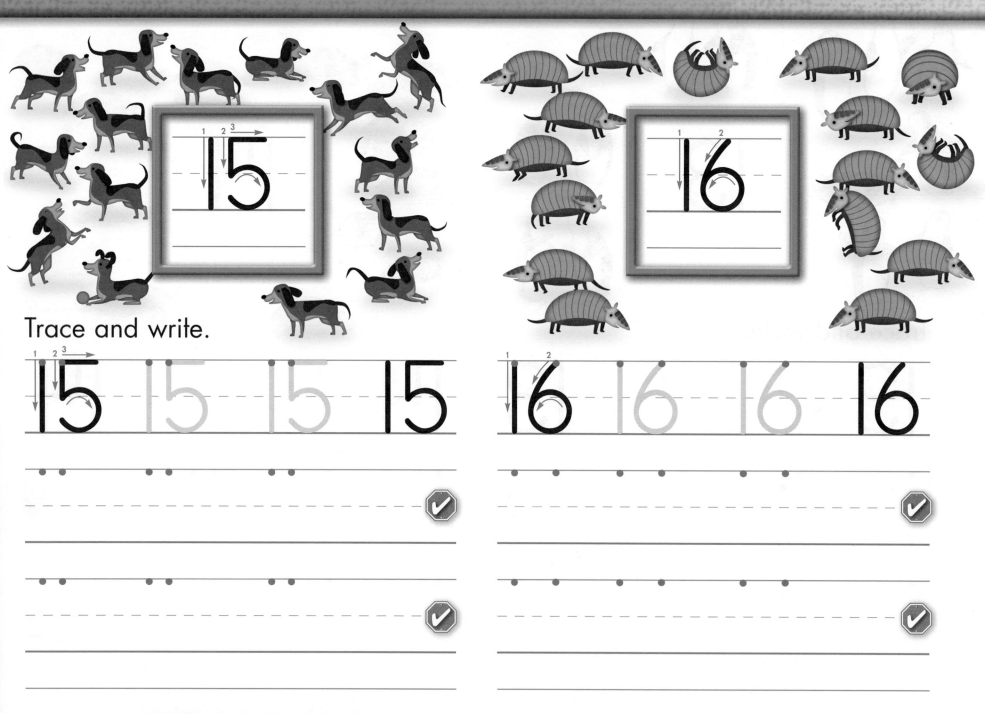

Trace and write.

15 15 15 15

16 16 16 16

Stroke descriptions to guide numeral formation at home:

15
1. Pull down straight. Lift.
2. Pull down straight. Circle forward. Lift.
3. Slide right.

16
1. Pull down straight. Lift.
2. Curve down; curve up and around.

Trace and write.

Stroke descriptions to guide numeral formation at home:

17
1. Pull down straight. Lift.
2. Slide right. Slant left.

18
1. Pull down straight. Lift.
2. Curve back; curve forward; slant up.

Trace and write.

Stroke descriptions to guide numeral formation at home:

19
1. Pull down straight. Lift.
2. Circle back all the way around. Pull down straight.

20
1. Curve forward; slant left. Slide right. Lift.
2. Curve down; curve up.

Practice

1, 2, 3, 4, 5
Penguins jump and dive.

6, 7, 8, 9, 10
Then they come up again.

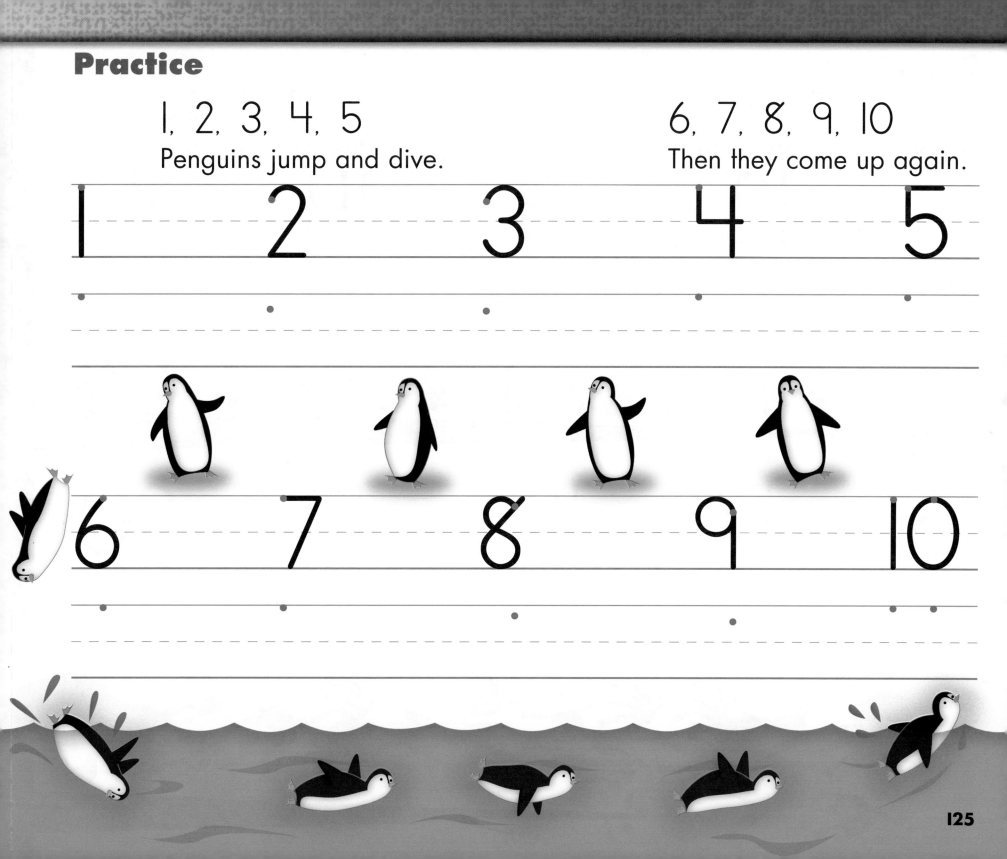

1   2   3   4   5

6   7   8   9   10

Practice

11, 12, 13, 14, 15
Birds stand and lean.

16, 17, 18, 19, 20
Then they fly away free.

11   12   13   14   15

16   17   18   19   20

Write your name.

Peter

Write letters you know.

Write your address.

Zaner-Bloser Basic Strokes

Circle Lines

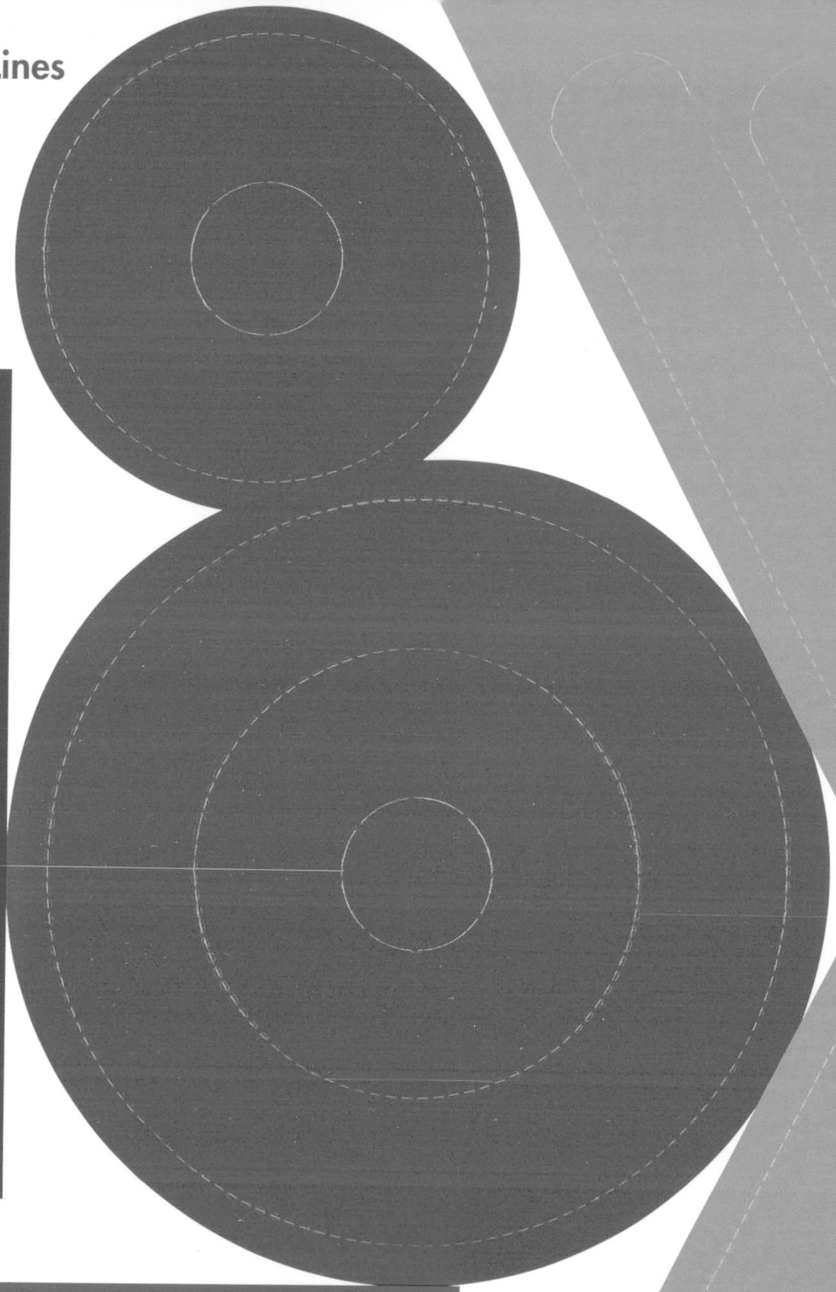

Slant Lines

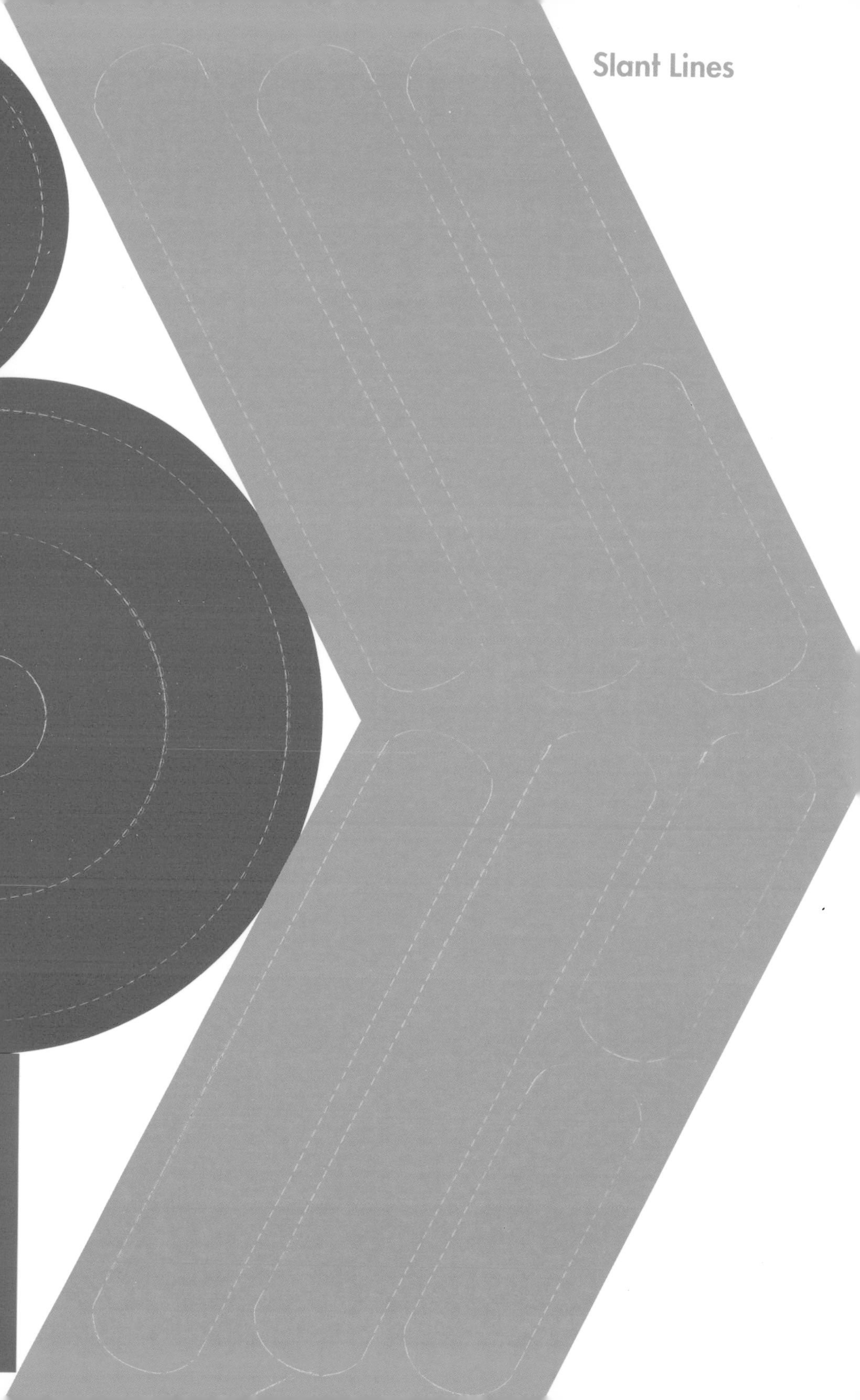

Vertical Lines

Horizontal Lines

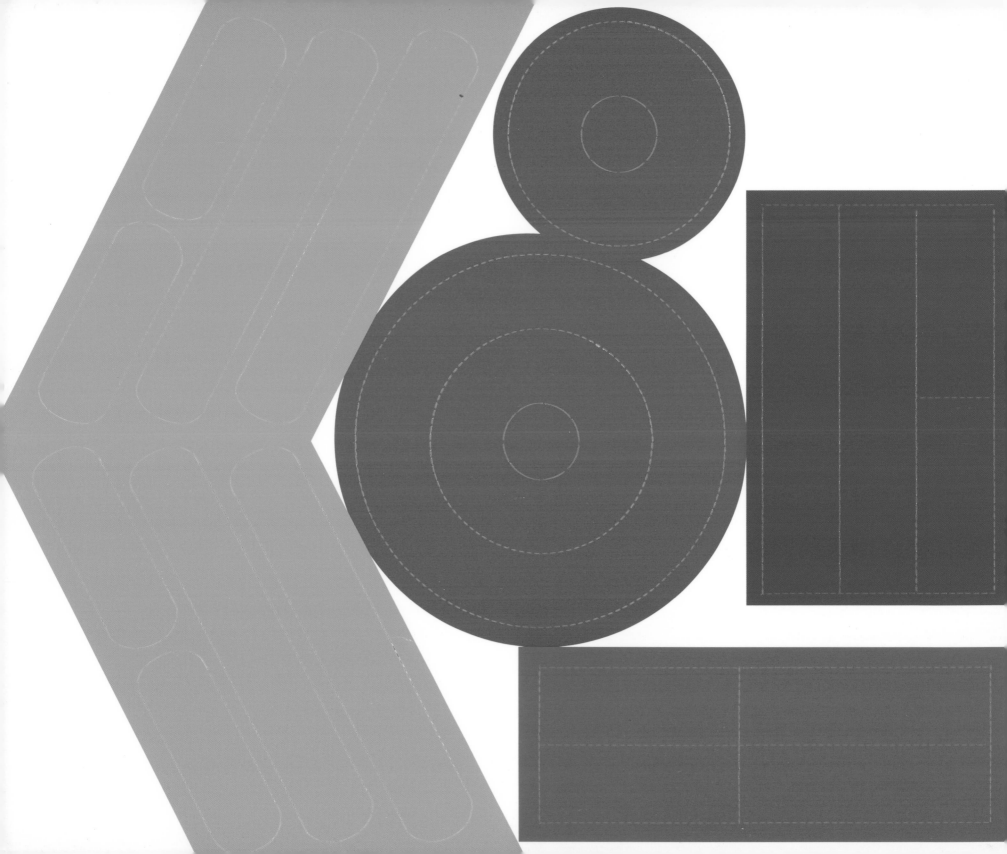

Happy Thought

The world is so full of a
number of things,
I'm sure we should all be
as happy as kings.

Robert Louis Stevenson

Help Lina find her way to the castle.

Finish

Start

Write Numerals

How many? Write the numeral.

_____

_____

_____

_____

_____

_____

_____

_____

_____

_____

Write Number Words

Write the numerals and the number words.

1 one

2 two

3 three

4 four

5 five

Write Number Words

Write the numerals and the number words.

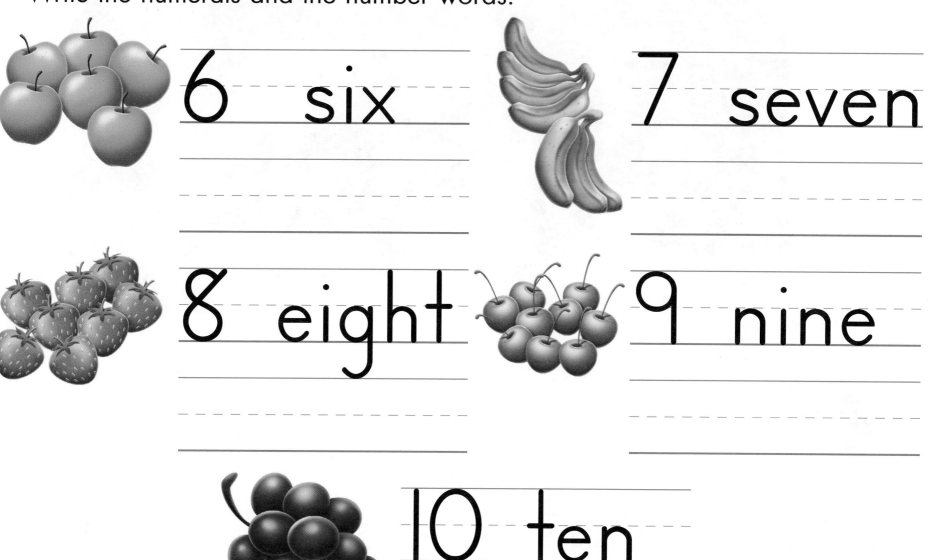

6 six

7 seven

8 eight

9 nine

10 ten

Write the words.

dog   cat   sun   pig

Write Words

Write the words.

ant   bee   cap   ball

Write Sentences

Write the sentences.

One dog plays piano.

Three dogs sing.

Write Sentences

Write the sentences.

One bear cooks food.

Three bears eat.

Write a Note

Write the note.

Dear Aunt Julia,

I miss you.   Get well.

Love, Ethan

Write an Invitation

Write the invitation.

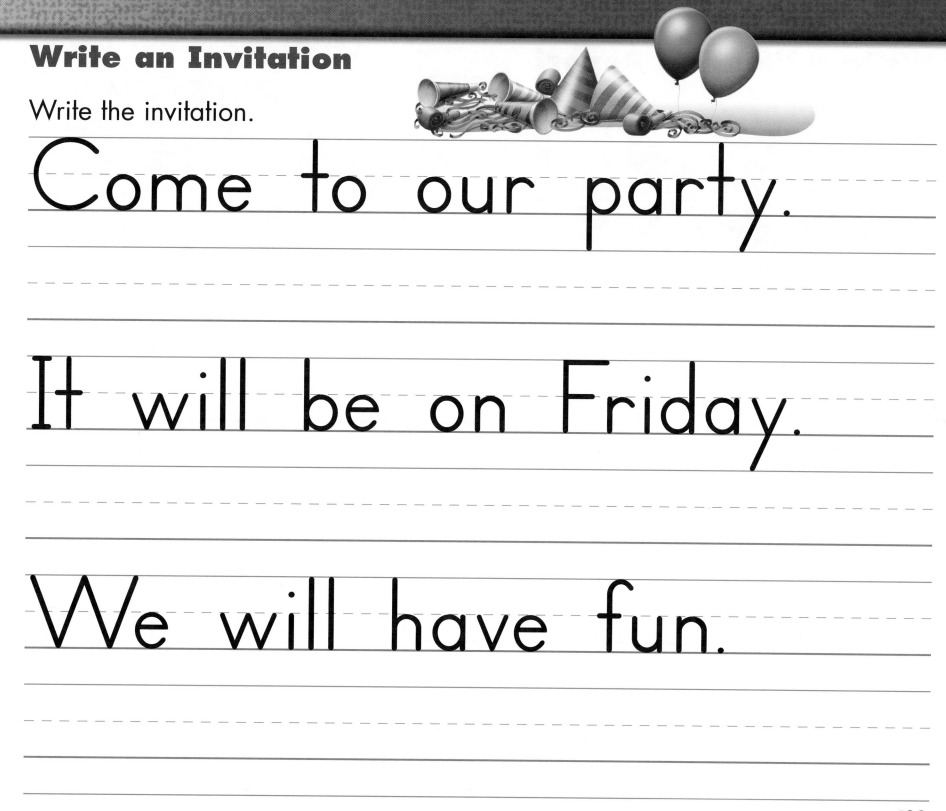

Come to our party.

It will be on Friday.

We will have fun.

Write a Weather Report

warm

cold

sunny

rainy

Choose words to complete the sentences. Write the sentences.

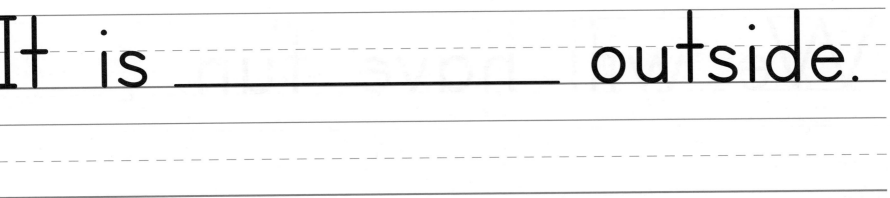

Today is _____.

It is _____ outside.

Draw a Picture

Draw a picture about weather. Write words about your picture.

Draw a picture.

Write words about your picture.

Record of Student's Handwriting Skills

Manuscript

	Needs Improvement	Shows Mastery		Needs Improvement	Shows Mastery
Uses good sitting position	☐	☐	Writes **u** and **U**	☐	☐
Positions paper correctly	☐	☐	Writes **s** and **S**	☐	☐
Holds pencil correctly	☐	☐	Writes **b** and **B**	☐	☐
Writes vertical lines	☐	☐	Writes **p** and **P**	☐	☐
Writes horizontal lines	☐	☐	Writes **r** and **R**	☐	☐
Writes backward circle lines	☐	☐	Writes **n** and **N**	☐	☐
Writes slant lines	☐	☐	Writes **m** and **M**	☐	☐
Writes forward circle lines	☐	☐	Writes **h** and **H**	☐	☐
Writes **l** and **L**	☐	☐	Writes **v** and **V**	☐	☐
Writes **i** and **I**	☐	☐	Writes **y** and **Y**	☐	☐
Writes **t** and **T**	☐	☐	Writes **w** and **W**	☐	☐
Writes **o** and **O**	☐	☐	Writes **x** and **X**	☐	☐
Writes **a** and **A**	☐	☐	Writes **k** and **K**	☐	☐
Writes **d** and **D**	☐	☐	Writes **z** and **Z**	☐	☐
Writes **c** and **C**	☐	☐	Writes a **.**	☐	☐
Writes **e** and **E**	☐	☐	Writes a **,**	☐	☐
Writes **f** and **F**	☐	☐	Writes numerals **1–5**	☐	☐
Writes **g** and **G**	☐	☐	Writes numerals **6–10**	☐	☐
Writes **j** and **J**	☐	☐	Writes numerals **11–15**	☐	☐
Writes **q** and **Q**	☐	☐	Writes numerals **16–20**	☐	☐

Index